Carboniferous
Bowland Fells to Pendle Hill

Edited by

PAUL KABRNA

Copyright

Published by Craven & Pendle Geological Society
First Edition, 2011

Typeset in Adobe Caslon Pro
Printed and bound by *The City Press Leeds Ltd.*
St. Ann's Mill, Commercial Road, Kirkstall, Leeds LS5 3AE

British Library Cataloguing in Publication Data
A catalogue record for this book is available from the British Library

ISBN 978-0-9555289-1-0

Dedicated to Yvonne James
(1950 - 2011)

About the Authors

Paul Kabrna

Paul joined the NE Lancashire Group of the Geologists' Association in 1970. In 1977 he graduated as a teacher of geology at Crewe & Alsager College. During the 1980s he served as Editor of the NE Lancashire Groups Proceedings, and then as Chairman. He then joined the Yorkshire Geological Society in 1989, serving on council from 1991 as Circular Editor for eleven years, and for three years as Web Editor. Along with his wife Yvonne James, and Paul Wignall of Leeds University, he co-founded Craven & Pendle Geological Society in 1990. Paul's first book on the seismologist John Milne was awarded second prize in the ENI Geological Challenge Award in 2007 - an annual award sponsored by the Italian oil and gas company.

Steve Donovan

Steve graduated in geology from Manchester in 1980, and was awarded his Ph.D. (1983) and D.Sc. (1994) by the University of Liverpool. He was a post-doctoral researcher at Trinity College, Dublin, in 1984, supported by the Royal Society. He has worked for the Natural Environment Research Council in Swindon (1985), the University of the West Indies in Jamaica (1986-1998), the Natural History Museum in London (1998-2001) and, since 2001, the NCB – Naturalis (formerly the Nationaal Natuurhistorisch Museum) in Leiden, The Netherlands. His principal research interests are fossil echinoderms (particularly his beloved crinoids), trace fossils, Caribbean geology and the history of geology. He has published over 300 books, monographs and research papers, mainly on palaeontology. He was awarded the 2008 Linnean Medal for Zoology.

David N. Lewis

Dave joined the Department of Palaeontology at the British Museum (Natural History) in October 1964. He started as a curator of brachiopods, and worked on corals for a short while until moving to the Echinoderm Section in 1969, where he stayed until retirement. During the echinoderm years, he worked with Dr. R. P. S. Jeffcries on the origin of chordates, curated the echinoderm collections, and published on a variety of topics. Dave's main interest was fossil echinoids, especially from the Tertiary and Palaeozoic, but he also contributed to papers on other echinoderms, trace fossils and curation. In 1990, he became Collections Manager for Fossil Invertebrates and Plants. Dave retired in July 2005 and is now a Scientific Associate in the Department of Palaeontology at the Natural History Museum in London.

Ian Kane

In 2004 Ian graduated from the University of Derby with a first class honours degree in geology. His final field-based project *The sedimentology and Ichnology of the Rough Rock and the Rough Rock Flags, (Yeadonian) of Cracken Edge, Derbyshire* earned him the Moore Medal from the Yorkshire Geological Society. In 2004 Ian undertook a Ph.D. at the University of Leeds, working on Upper Cretaceous submarine channel systems in Baja California, Mexico. In 2007, upon completion of his Ph.D., Ian began postdoctoral research on the Carboniferous Pendle Grit. In 2008 he was awarded the Yorkshire Geological Society Fearnsides Prize for promise in geological research and geological sciences. Ian is now a research geologist with Statoil ASA in Bergen, Norway.

Contents

GEOLOGICAL SOCIETY

Craven & Pendle Geological Society was founded in 1990 to promote local interest in the geological sciences. To achieve this goal seven indoor lectures and five outdoor field meetings are arranged each year. At the time of writing the indoor meetings are held on Friday evenings at the Rainhall Centre in Barnoldswick. Past themes have included *Volcanic eruptions into Iceland's glaciers,* and the topical *UK's energy needs . . . . in a future without North Sea oil and gas.* Field meetings are wide ranging and have included visits to Runswick Bay on the east coast of North Yorkshire, Whitbarrow in South Lakeland, Alderley Edge in Cheshire, and Anglesey in North Wales. Membership to the Society is by payment of an annual subscription fee. A digital résumé of each indoor lecture is produced for members only. Non-members are welcome at £2.00 per meeting. Further information is available at www.cpgs.org.uk.

Members of the CPGS gather on the A59 Chatburn Bypass road cutting east side, near the village of Chatburn. This locality is the current reference section for the Chatburn Limestone Formation. Photo © Yvonne James (1992).

Foreword

The area of northern Lancashire stretching from the Bowland Fells to the hill of Pendle is a mixture of rugged moorland and quiet pastoral valleys. Unlike the limestone uplands of the Yorkshire Dales immediately to the north it receives relatively little attention from tourists and is consequently blessed with many beautiful and tranquil locations. Surprisingly, this disregard also applies to the degree of geological study that has been undertaken in the region, particularly in recent decades, despite the fact it contains some of the most varied and fascinating Carboniferous geology to be found anywhere in the country. Thus, we can thank Paul Kabrna for assembling a team of experts to produce the first book to specifically focus on the geology of the area, known to most as the Craven Basin.

For much of the Carboniferous Period the Craven Basin recorded relatively deep-water conditions that lay south of the stable, slowly subsiding, shallow-water Askrigg Block. Undoubtedly the most celebrated rocks encountered in the Basin are reef mounds or knolls and Paul provides an accessible introduction to these fascinating features and their associated strata. There is much we do not understand about these mounds – we have no modern analogues – for example how were they formed and why were they only common for a brief interval in the Early Carboniferous? Read what Paul has to say, see the rocks in the field and ponder.

The Waulsortian mounds are also famous for their fabulous echinoderm fauna, and here for the first time Stephen Donovan and David Lewis have provided an authoritative description of this important and exceptionally preserved fauna. The disarticulated remains of crinoids are familiar when cursorily glancing at most Carboniferous limestones but, in the rocks around Clitheroe, we find complete cups (calyxes) of crinoids, complete blastoids and echinoids. Now Palaeozoic echinoid remains are rare indeed but to find them with their plates still articulated is truly exceptional. The reason for such preservation is, like many other features of the Waulsortian mounds, still a mystery, but you can see them illustrated here in all their glory.

By the end of the Early Carboniferous the limestones were giving way to an inundation of terrigenous sediment, initially dark muds (now the Bowland Shale) and ultimately a major influx of sand that formed the deep-water turbidite fan that constitutes the Pendle Grit. This is a tough rock and it forms the impressive uplands around Clitheroe. Study of these strata is important because they provide good analogues for many oilfield reservoirs and, of more direct economic significance, they are the source of road aggregate in working quarries in the area. Nonetheless, like the other rocks in the region, geological attention has languished in recent decades but it is now undergoing something of a renaissance. This is thanks to the almost single-handed research efforts of Ian Kane, and here he provides a valuable introduction to both the rocks and the processes that formed them.

Enjoy reading about these diverse rocks and their fossils and when you have done so I encourage you to visit them in the field using the field guides provided. You will not find many areas in the UK where carbonate reef mounds, black shales, and major sand bodies can all be seen within a few kilometres of each other.

Paul Wignall
University of Leeds,
September 2011.

Introduction

Paul Kabrna

The aim of this book is to highlight the geological heritage in an area geographically known as the Craven Lowlands (fig. 1) which occupies part of the counties of Lancashire and Yorkshire. Geologists usually refer to this area as either the Craven Basin (Hudson, 1933) or Bowland Basin (Ramsbottom, 1974). However, the content of our book focuses on a small part of the Craven Basin which we refer to as the Bowland Sub-Basin. The scenically attractive landscape of this area is a reflection of how geological processes millions of years ago have combined to mould the rocks into their present day configuration. As the region is composed almost entirely of Carboniferous sedimentary rocks you would imagine that the task would be quite straightforward, however, the combination of powerful Earth forces that deformed the rocks by faulting and folding, and the geologically-recent invading ice sheets that deposited a blanket of boulder clay (till) on top of the rocks, conspired to make the Bowland Sub-Basin a geologically complex Carboniferous landscape.

Local History

Steeped in history and folklore, Pendle Hill rises to 557 m and is just short of being a mountain by about 55 m. The hill will always be famously associated with the Pendle Witches, and the foundation of the Quaker movement. The story of the Pendle Witch trials is perhaps the best known example of alleged witchcraft in English history. Following the trials ten local people were executed in Lancaster on the 20th August 1612 for practising witchcraft. The hill continues to be associated with witchcraft and every Halloween locals and visitors have been known to trek to the summit.

In 1652 George Fox claimed to have had a vision while on top of Pendle Hill during the early years of the Religious Society of Friends (Quakers). *We came near a very great high hill, called Pendle-hill, and I was moved of the Lord to go up to the top of it; which I did with much ado, it was so very steep and high. When I was come to the top, I saw the sea bordering upon Lancashire. From*

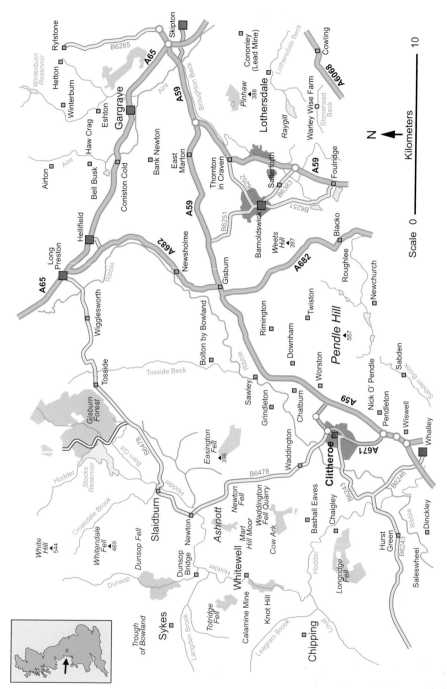

Fig. 1 Location map of the main towns, villages and roads in the Craven Lowlands

the top of this hill the Lord let me see in what places he had a great people to be gathered. As I went down I found a spring of water in the side of the hill, with which I refreshed myself, having eaten or drank but little several days before (Jones, 1908). Today, the name Pendle remains strongly linked with the Quakers, giving its name to their centre of learning in the USA.

Along the flanks of Pendle Hill in Faughs Delf Quarry southwest of Newchurch-in-Pendle, there is a sculpture of a face depicted into the rock of a man which resembles one of the many examples of a 'Green Man' (fig.2) found throughout the country and in

Fig. 2   A Green Man sculptured into Warley Wise Grit. Scale: two pence coin below the chin. Photo © Yvonne James

many cultures around the world. Perhaps the origin of this Green Man is not shrouded in history, but was in fact carved by one of the quarrymen, and the name Green Man assigned to this carving after Green Hill which lies in close proximity to the quarry.

Scientific experiments have also had a part to play in the history of Pendle Hill. Richard Towneley (1629-1707) was a mathematician, astronomer and natural philosopher. He was member of a Catholic gentry family from Towneley Hall, a large country house on the outskirts of Burnley. Whilst working with other local collaborators, he conducted experiments into the relationship between air pressure and volume at different altitudes on Pendle Hill. Later in 1662, Robert Boyle was able to publish what is now known as Boyle's Law but what he referred to as Mr Towneley's hypothesis.

More recently, the picturesque village of Downham at the foot of Pendle Hill was the location for the filming of the classic 1960s British movie *Whistle Down the Wind,* and was also the setting for the BBC series *Born and Bred.*

A number of villages date back to Anglo Saxon times, many of which are mentioned in the Doomsday Book. The villages are typical estate villages where buildings are of a similar age and design, for example, Downham and Slaidburn. Others are more haphazard farming settlements or industrial hamlets. Recommended heritage sites for visitors to the region include: Clitheroe Castle and the recently renovated Castle Museum, the 14th century Whalley Abbey, the 12th century Sawley Abbey, and the historic 16th century Stonyhurst College at Hurst Green. The landscape around Hurst Green is said to have been influential in J. R. R. Tolkien's writing as he was creating the *Lord of the Rings* trilogy. The distinguished author Sir Arthur Conan Doyle was a scholar at Stonyhurst College from September 1868. It is likely that some of the principal characters featured in his books may have been based on, or at least influenced by, people he had known at Stonyhurst.

For the visitors with geographical interests, Dunsop Bridge, besides being the entrance to the Trough of Bowland, has been declared as the official geographical centre of the British Isles by the Ordnance Survey. The explorer Sir Ranulph Fiennes unveiled a plaque that verifies this fact.

Physical Features

The misleading ancient terms 'Forest of Bowland' and 'Forest of Pendle' appear on most Ordnance Survey maps even though they are no longer forested! The Forest of Bowland covers a substantial part of the region and is an Area of Outstanding Natural Beauty (AONB) with just over 10% designated as a Site of Special Scientific Interest (SSSI) for its habitats and geological features. The Bowland Fells are cut by narrow wooded valleys and discrete cloughs that drain the moorland heights. Impressive upland landscapes include Pendle Hill, Longridge Fell, Beacon Fell, Newton Fell and Marl Hill Moor. These high moorland escarpments are composed of tough sandstones and gritstones whilst the intervening lowland areas by contrast are dominated by softer mudstones. The occasional abrupt transition into higher ground usually indicates the presence of limestone knolls which add to the complexity of the geological history of the region.

The current drainage network reflects the regions glacial legacy, with erosion perhaps accentuated by glacial meltwaters capturing the Hodder headwaters at the expense of the formerly westward-draining Loud valley, and Ribble headwaters at the expense of the eastward-draining Aire (Harvey, 1985, 1997a). Apart from the Aire which crosses the northeast corner of the region, all the important streams belong to the Ribble catchment. The Ribble is the largest river system in Lancashire. It rises in the Yorkshire Dales National Park and flows south and west eventually reaching the Irish Sea through an estuary extending from Preston. For much of its course from Newsholme to Dinckley, the Ribble meanders through wide terraced alluvial flats. Near Gisburn it cuts a gorge through gently dipping Carboniferous limestone. *Anciently the Ribble formed a political boundary between north and south, as well as an important routeway from east to west; and today it still marks a stark contrast between rural countryside to the north and industrial landscapes to the south* (Greenhalgh, 2008).

The Hodder flows south and drains much of the Bowland Fells. All but the last kilometre of its course passes through this scenic area. The upper reaches of the river feed Stocks Reservoir near Slaidburn which provides water mainly for the Fylde area of Lancashire. After exiting the reservoir the Hodder continues in a general southward direction. Most notable among the feeders of the Hodder are Croasdale Brook, Easington Brook, the River Dunsop, Langden Brook, and the River Loud. As the Hodder skirts Longridge Fell prior to joining the Ribble near Great Mitton, its course follows a narrower path almost gorge-like through well-wooded surroundings.

The River Aire is a major river in Yorkshire with an intriguing history regarding its source in Malhamdale. The underground course of the Aire was first investigated at the end of the 19th century when members of the Yorkshire Geological & Polytechnic Society (now the Yorkshire Geological Society) conducted a series of classic water tracing experiments. Their results indicated a complex hydrology for the area with underground water also resurging from Aire Head Springs (to the south of Malham village). The uncertainty regarding the source persisted for many years with some favouring the source of the Aire to be Malham Cove whilst others have preferred Aire Head Springs. Recently the Cave Diving Group investigated the hydrology and concluded that *this important resurgence, located at the base of the celebrated Malham Cove in North Yorkshire, drains a large area of limestone to the north and west. It is the source of the River Aire, which in the valley just downstream provided the inspiration for Charles Kingsley's book* The Water Babies (1863) (Cordingley, 2010). From Malham, the Aire flows through Gargrave and Skipton prior to entering West Yorkshire.

Industry

In the 16th century the building trade took a significant step forward when mortar and plaster replaced timber or wattle and daub structures. This led to an increased demand for lime in addition to its traditional use for agricultural purposes. Although not in the Craven Lowlands, Sheddon Valley near Burnley has an interesting history. It is not in a limestone area, however, there are the remains of a pre-industrial lime burning enterprise. The resourceful workers dug out limestone boulders from the glacial drift and burned for lime; the old lime kilns testify to this remarkable initiative.

Although pastoral farming is still deeply rooted in the region, industrial growth brought in much needed economic prosperity. The beginning of the 19th century heralded the arrival of steam powered manufacture, better roads, canals and railways. The opening of the railway connection from Clitheroe to Manchester was central to the success of the local lime works.

Bold Venture lime works in Chatburn was the largest local industry that had been quarrying limestone for over 400 years for building stone, and to burn for agricultural use. In 1850 the lime works successfully expanded its operations. Not long after Coplow lime works and Bellmanpark lime works began operations significantly adding to the economic prosperity of Clitheroe and Chatburn. In 1935 the cement works were purchased by Ribblesdale Cement Ltd and in 1986 it was renamed Castle Cement. The business is now part of Hanson Heidelberg Cement Group, the current owner of the site since 1999. Peter del Strother (General Manager Technical retired) has written a book titled *The History of Ribblesdale Cement* which is dedicated to all Ribblesdale employees, past and present. The book was published by Castle Cement in 2008. At the time of writing, Castle Cement has one operating kiln and a work force of about 110. There are known quarry reserves of 30 years (fig.3), and more than one million tonnes of limestone are quarried every year for an annual production of 0.8 million tonnes of cement. Cement from Ribblesdale has been used in several major architectural projects including Manchester International Airport, Heysham Nuclear Power Station, Manchester Magistrates Court, Manchester United football stadium, and Liverpool's Roman Catholic Cathedral. The works has supplied materials more recently for the Frodsham Railway Bridge over the M56 construction project.

Fig. 3 Looking west into Castle Cement's Lanehead Quarry (Chatburn Limestone Formation). In the distance lies the Vale of Chipping. The distant hills from left to right are Longridge Fell, Parlick, Fair Snape Fell and Totridge Fell.

Another rock type of economic value in the region is sandstone. There are numerous disused quarries on Longridge Fell, Pendle Hill and in Salterforth (fig. 4) near Barnoldswick which have all exploited thick deposits of Pendle Grit. Waddington Fell Quarry is an active working Pendle Grit quarry located on the summit 6 km north of Clitheroe and 3.5 km north of the

Fig. 4 Park Close Quarry (Pendle Grit) in Salterforth around 1890. The grit was used in the construction of parts of the Leeds-Liverpool Canal. The top level of the quarry is now a residential caravan park. Scale: Four people stood by the crane.

village of Waddington. The quarry on Waddington Fell can be traced back to the 14th century when Pendle Grit was used to build St. Helen's Church in Waddington. Aggregate Industries are the current owners of the quarry. Their product range includes hand-carved fireplaces, bespoke carving and engraving, and crushed washed sand for use in concrete mixes. The geologically older Pendleside Sandstone was of more limited economic value being mainly restricted to use as a local building stone.

Exploitation of metaliferous mineral deposits in the region can be traced back to Roman times. Lead (galena) and zinc (sphalerite) have been worked from twelve locations over the past 500 years until the 1930s when Cononley lead mine, 6 km south of Skipton in North Yorkshire, ceased working.

The next chapter on History and Research summarises early mineralisation and the distinguished contribution of geologists who made significant advances in our understanding of Carboniferous geology of the area.

Fig. 5 The inaugural field excursion of Craven & Pendle Geological Society was held in Barnoldswick in September 1990. Left to right: Yvonne James, Wallace Berry, Pat Sutcliffe, Vincent Nuttall, April Marsden, and Ron Duerden.

Chapter 1

History and Research

Paul Kabrna

In 1822 Rev. William D. Conybeare (1787-1857) and William Phillips (1775-1828) created the Carboniferous as a formal stratigraphic term for a period of geological time where coal, limestone and sandstone were the dominant rock types. They grouped these rock types chronologically under the following headings (the Mountain Limestone being the oldest):

I   Coal Measures
II   Millstone Grit
III   Mountain Limestone

Originally Conybeare and Phillips also included the Old Red Sandstone within the Carboniferous, but this was later reassigned to the older Devonian Period.

In contrast to the Conybeare scheme, Winch (1817) proposed that Carboniferous rocks in the north of England should be separated into an upper series, the 'coal measures', and a lower, the 'lead-mine measures'. Both Winch and Conybeare had recognised the economic importance of strata of Carboniferous age. During the next 200 years the advancement in our understanding of Carboniferous geology would be driven by the continuing search for natural resources such as oil, gas, and aggregate materials (sand, gravel and limestone) for the construction industry.

Mineralisation

As early as the 16th century, common minerals such as galena (lead), baryte and subordinate zinc and copper have been mined from a variety of Carboniferous host rocks in the Bowland Sub-Basin. Exploitation has generally been through small-scale mining activity and has therefore had little economic impact.

In the Ribble valley north of Pendle Hill, Skelleron Mine near Rimington worked galena (PbS), barytes (BaSO$_4$) and zinc (ZnS). In 1877 twenty underground miners and eight surface workers retrieved 5 tons of zinc. Between 1880 and 1881 a new shaft enabled the miners to extract nearly 2 000 tons of barytes. A further venture in 1920 only yielded 80 tons before the miners stopped working. The final operation in Skelleron was early in the 1950s when two students produced several tons of barytes.

Another successful mining operation for barytes took place at Raygill Quarry in Lothersdale near Skipton. In 1845 rich veins of barytes were discovered making Raygill the largest producer of barytes in the country.

Of minor economic significance are the small amounts of metalliferous mineral deposits found in the Hodder valley, and near Sykes farm in the Trough of Bowland. At Sykes galena ore was retrieved from the Hetton Beck Limestone in the core of Sykes Anticline. At Ashnott near Newton mineralisation occurs in association with limestone on Ashnott knoll. This is also the case at Dinkling Green where another limestone knoll has been worked for small pockets of zinc carbonate ore or smithsonite, also known as calamine (De Rance, 1873).

Summary of previous research

John Phillips (1800-1874) was the nephew and protégé of William Smith (1769-1839) the Father of English Geology. Phillips was a most remarkable geologist in his own right. In 1841 he proposed the terms Palaeozoic (ancient life), Mesozoic (middle life) and Cainozoic (recent life); all three terms are used today with the Carboniferous Period being an integral part of the Palaeozoic era. He was a prolific field geologist and author of the classic *Illustrations of the geology of Yorkshire* Part 2 *The Mountain Limestone District* (1836) which contains an excellent review of the geological setting of the area. The many descriptions of fossils were illustrated by Phillips's original sketches. From his research he was able to define for the first time the boundary between the Carboniferous Limestone and the Millstone Grit. He also introduced the term Bowland Shale.

Phillips benefited from the generosity of Preston chemist William Gilbertson (1788-1845) who became known for his formidable collection of fossils from the Craven Lowlands which was said by Phillips to be 'unrivalled at that time'. Rather than publishing his own work, Gilbertson passed on his collection and notes to Phillips who then went on to describe numerous Carboniferous ammonoids and crinoids for the first time. In York on the 1st March 1836 Phillips stated:

> But my greatest obligation is to Mr Gilbertson of Preston, a naturalist of high acquirements, who has for many years explored with exceeding diligence and acumen a region of mountain limestone remarkably rich in organic remains. The collection which he has amassed from the small district of Bolland is at this moment unrivalled, and he has done for me, without solicitation, what is seldom granted to the most urgent entreaty; he has sent me for deliberate examination, at convenient intervals, the whole of his magnificent collection, accompanied by remarks dictated by long experience and a sound judgment. He had proposed to publish an account of his discoveries, and especially of the Crinoidea for which no man in Europe had equal materials, and had made a great number of careful drawings for the purpose; but all these, as well as the specimens, he placed at my disposal—a striking proof of liberal and genuine devotion to science.

The collection was eventually purchased by the Zoology Department of the British Museum in 1841 and is presently housed in the Palaeontology Department of the Natural History Museum, London (NHM). The importance of fossil echinoderms in the Clitheroe District is discussed in detail in Chapter 3 by Donovan & Lewis.

Our understanding of Carboniferous geology accelerated with the arrival of the officers of the Geological Survey. The name Richard Hill Tiddeman (1842-1917) is synonymous with mapping the district during the Primary Survey between 1870 and 1880, and the publication of the one inch to a mile sheet in 1892. The mapping by the Geological Survey team produced the following succession:

Classification of Carboniferous rocks (after Tiddeman, 1892)

Millstone Grit
Bowland Shales .... 300 - 1000 feet
Pendleside Grit .... inconstant
Pendleside Limestone .... 0-500 feet
Shales with Limestone .... 2500 feet maximum
Clitheroe Limestone .... 3250 feet exposed; base not reached

Tiddeman is also remembered for his work on the formation of 'reef knolls', and for the recognition of the Middle Craven Fault which is best viewed near Malham. In 1872 Tiddeman also published his findings on the glaciation of north Lancashire, a precursor to a particular fine study on the glacial geology of East Lancashire by Albert Jowett in 1914. In the 1870s Tiddeman collaborated with William Boyd Dawkins on the large-scale excavation of Quaternary deposits in Victoria Cave near Settle in north Yorkshire, and from 1874 to 1878 directed the investigation. In 1911 he was presented with the Murchison Medal by the Geological Society of London, and the Yorkshire Geological Society elected him their President in 1914.

The early 20th century geologists focused on palaeontology as an adjunct to stratigraphy. Arthur Vaughan (1905) used fossils (predominantly corals and brachiopods) to establish a succession in Lower Carboniferous strata in the Bristol district. Vaughan's paper on the *Palaeontological Sequence in the Carboniferous Limestone of the Bristol Area* was published by the Geological Society in 1905. 'It was one of the most influential papers to have appeared in the Journal and pioneered biostratigraphical subdivision of the Carboniferous Limestone in Britain, whilst providing one of the first detailed commentaries on the principles of biostratigraphy' (Riley, 1993 pp. 427). Vaughan's ideas were tested and extended in the Settle district in 1924 by E. J. Garwood (1864-1949) and E. Goodyear (1879-1959). However, Vaughan's scheme of subdividing Carboniferous limestones could not easily be extended to the more muddy strata of the Bowland Sub-Basin due to a distinct lack of rich coral / brachiopod faunas.

An alternative approach to subdividing local rocks of the Bowland Sub-Basin was initiated by Wheelton Hind (1918) who recognised the value of using ammonoids for zoning deep water mudrocks. The importance of Hind's ammonoid work was advanced by William Sawney Bisat (1886-1973). Bisat was an engineer and amateur geologist who published a classic account of Carboniferous goniatites in the north of England in 1924. In describing the goniatite zones, Bisat enabled the stratigrapher to accurately subdivide shale-dominated sequences, not just in the north of England, but throughout Europe and the USA. Prior to this monumental work there had been gross miscorrelations, particularly in Namurian stratigraphy. Of all the awards and honours Bisat received for his distinguished contribution to biostratigraphy, the one he probably coveted most was the election to the

Fellowship of the Royal Society, an exceptional honour rarely achieved by an amateur (Baldwin, 2004).

Two other distinguished geologists who worked on local Carboniferous rocks were Robert George Spencer Hudson (Skipton area, 1927, 1933, 1944), and Donald Parkinson (Clitheroe, Pendle Hill and Slaidburn, 1926, 1935, 1936, 1964).

Hudson (1895-1965) was a student of E. J. Garwood at University College, London and subsequently became Professor of Geology at Leeds University. During his quarter century in Yorkshire, he published over fifty papers on the Carboniferous of the Craven area. Working with Bisat, Hudson's work on the Yoredale Series added stratigraphical support for Tiddeman's theory that the limestones of the Bowland Forest region were earlier in age than had been previously thought. It was Hudson who, in 1938, gave the name Askrigg Block to the rigid block underlying northwest Yorkshire which forms the northern boundary of the Craven Basin, separated by the Craven Fault Zone. He fully demonstrated the relationships between the Yoredale lithological and faunal facies and contemporaneous crustal movements. Working first with G. H. Mitchell and later with G. Cotton, he also produced comparisons with the shell-reef faunas of the southern margins of the basin on the flanks of the Derbyshire massif. Hudson's work in the Craven area was largely responsible for his being awarded the D. Sc. (1929), his receipt of the Geological Society's Murchison medal (1958) and his election as a Fellow of the Royal Society (1961). A much fuller account of the life and work of Hudson is available in the recently published book 'Hud: The Life And Work Of Robert George Spencer Hudson' by William Hudson, ISBN-978-0981555621.

Donald Parkinson (1891-1974) was born in Clitheroe and educated at the local council school until he was 13 years old. He then joined the weekly 'Clitheroe Advertiser' where he became a compositor. During World War I while serving in France he was seriously wounded. The injury resulted in Parkinson having a permanent limp. Although he had to rely on the support of a walking stick, he remained remarkably agile when conducting field work. In 1918 he obtained a position with the Dunlop Rubber Company in Birmingham. In 1923 at the age of 32 he graduated from Birmingham University with first-class honours in Geology, obtaining a Ph.D. two years later. His geological interests often brought him back to Clitheroe. Parkinson (1926) adopted the terminology used by the Geological Survey in 1875 in describing the geology around Clitheroe. He introduced the formal name Chatburn Limestone, and divided the knoll series into a lower Coplow Knoll Series and an upper Salthill-Worsaw Knoll Series. Parkinson reintroduced the term Worston Shale Series and contributed a new name, the Pendleside Limestone Series. For his paper of 1954, *Quantitative Studies of Brachiopods from the Lower Carboniferous Reef Limestones of England*, he received the award of Best Paper of the Year in the Journal of Paleontology, a considerable achievement for a British amateur in a professional American journal. Parkinson's contributions to geology were recognised by the awards of the Wollaston Fund in 1927, the R. H. Worth Prize in 1957, and in 1968 the Yorkshire Geological Society (YGS) presented him with the John Phillips Medal.

The Primary Survey made by Tiddeman was revisited when the British Geological Survey produced the *Geology of the Country Around Clitheroe and Nelson* (Earp et al., 1961). This memoir for the last 50 years has been an important source of information regarding the geology of the Bowland Sub-Basin. The memoir also covers the geology in the districts of Burnley, Colne and Nelson in NE Lancashire, an area which is dominated by rocks of the Millstone Grit Group and the Coal Measures. The 125 cm thick Arley coal seam was one of the most important resources in the Burnley Coalfield bringing considerable economic prosperity to the region.

W. H. C. (Bill) Ramsbottom (1926-2004) graduated from Clare College Cambridge in 1947. In the same year he joined the Geological Survey in London. He completed his Ph.D. on Lower Palaeozoic crinoids at Chelsea Polytechnic College (University of London) in 1954. As an officer of the British Geological Survey working in the Leeds office, he was their expert on palaeontology and stratigraphy of the Carboniferous Period. Ramsbottom was a pioneer in the use of global changes in sea level for stratigraphic correlation. This has now become very important in oil exploration around the world. Although he was thought of as simply being a 'fossil man', his studies were less interested in systematic palaeontology than in how biostratigraphical collecting could be linked with lithostratigraphy, sedimentology and tectonics to create a greater overall understanding of Carboniferous systems. Ramsbottom (1973, 1977) saw that correlating the complex lithologies of the British Carboniferous could be simplified by using 'mesothems'; units of strata defined by changing sea level. These ideas were presented in some detail in the Yorkshire Geological Society *Proceedings* during the 1970s and 1980s. He was awarded the Yorkshire Geological Society's Phillips Medal in 1972 and was President in 1975-76. A thorough account of the Dinantian and Namurian by Ramsbottom can be found in *The geology and mineral resources of Yorkshire (1974)* Editors: Rayner, D. H. & Hemingway J. E., pp. 47-87 (published by the YGS). Ramsbottom was also co-founder of the Palaeontological Association of which he was President in 1980-82. He also served on the Subcommission of Carboniferous Stratigraphy. Bill Ramsbottom was a great supporter of other workers investigations of Carboniferous systems and many colleagues and research students benefited from his advice.

Tiddeman, Hudson, Parkinson, and Ramsbottom had set the scene for a new generation of geologists to enter the debate one of whom was Nick Riley. Nicholas J. Riley was born on 28 February 1956. He obtained a B.Sc. in Geology and Zoology at the University of Bristol in 1977. In 1981 he completed his Ph.D. in Geology at the University of Bristol on research concerning early Viséan ammonoids and trilobites of the Bowland Sub-Basin (incidentally Bill Ramsbottom was one of his supervisors). From 1980, up to Nick joining the BGS Senior Management Team, he was the main provider of stratigraphic interpretation of Carboniferous sequences. In 2003 he was awarded the MBE by Her Majesty the Queen for services to UK geosciences. Since 2004 he has been Coordinator and President of the European Research Network of Excellence on the geological storage of CO_2 'CO$_2$GeoNet', and from 2005 part of the Sustainable & Renewable Energy Programme at BGS. Currently Nick is Head of Science Policy (Europe) & Grantsmanship.

The next chapter discusses the lithostratigraphy and depositional history of the Bowland Sub-Basin as it evolved from a carbonate shelf / ramp setting into a deep water dysaerobic/anoxic environment (Tournaisian-Viséan stages).

The reference lists for the Introduction and Chapter 1 are consolidated with those of Chapter 2.

Nick Riley (1991) examining a section across the Mid-Carboniferous Boundary interval in the banks of Well Beck, northwest of Summersgill in the Lancaster Fells Sub-Basin. The grey silty mudstones and black shales, with nodular ironstones and wackestones belong to the Crossdale Mudstone Formation.

Chapter 2

Depositional history (Tournaisian - Viséan) of the Bowland Sub-Basin.

Paul Kabrna

The oldest Carboniferous rocks at outcrop are sedimentary limestones and mudstones which were deposited in tropical seas. By contrast, younger sandstone and millstone grit deposits originate from large rivers which flowed into the sea from the north and east marking a transition into a humid equatorial environment. In order for these different types of sedimentary rocks to be deposited in tropical and equatorial environments, what we now know as Great Britain must have been near to the equator at one time. The explanation lies in continental drift. At the beginning of the Carboniferous Period 359.2 million years ago the Earth was made up of two continental landmasses known as Laurussia (Laurasia) and Gondwana. Great Britain was situated on the southern margin of Laurussia as marked by the red square in Figure 1 below.

Fig. 1   Mississippian palaeogeographic reconstruction.
Artwork © Ron Blakey, Northern Arizona University, USA

- 9 -

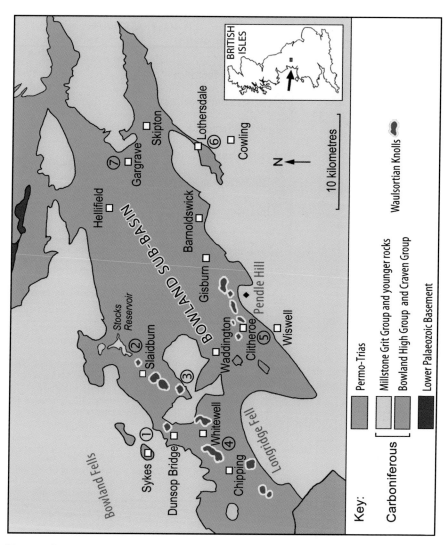

Fig. 2   Simplified map of the geology of the Bowland Sub-Basin within the Craven Basin of northern England. The strata in orange is predominantly Bowland Shale and Pendle Grit with younger Carboniferous deposits to the south and southwest of Cowling. The blue colour is mainly limestone, siltstone and mudstone. The circled numbers 1 to 7 represent the approximate location of field excursions in Chapter 5.

SYSTEM	SUB-SYSTEM	GLOBAL STAGE	WEST EU	DATE (MA)	UK	LITHOSTRATIGRAPHY Formations	Members / Beds
C A R B O N I F E R O U S	PENNSYLVANIAN (part)	Bashkirian (part)	Namurian		Millstone Grit Group	Rossendale Formation	
						Marsden Formation	
						Hebden Formation	Parsonage Sandstone
		Serpukhovian		322.8		Samlesbury Formation	Sabden Shales
						Silsden Formation	
						Pendleton Formation	Warley Wise Grit / Surgill Shale / Pendle Grit
	MISSISSIPPIAN			330	Craven Group	Bowland Shale Formation	Hind Sandstone / Pendleside Sandstone / Ravensholme Limestone / Park Style Limestone
		Viséan	Viséan			Pendleside Limestone Formation	Rad Brook Mudstone
						Hodderense Limestone Formation	
						Hodder Mudstone Formation	Twiston Sandstone / Chaigley Limestone / Embsay Limestone / Rain Gill Limestone / Buckbanks Sandstone / Leagram Mudstone / Hetton Beck Limestone / Whitemore Limestone / Phynis Mudstone / Limekiln Wood Limestone
				346.3	Bowland High Group	∿∿∿ UNCONFORMITY ∿∿∿	
						Clitheroe Limestone Formation	Bellman Limestone / Peach Quarry Limestone / Coplow Limestone / Thornton Limestone
		Tournaisian	Tournaisian			Chatburn Limestone Formation	Bold Venture Beds / Bankfield East Beds / Horrocksford Beds / Gisburn Cotes Beds
				359.2			

Fig. 3 Lithostratigraphic succession in the Bowland Sub-Basin (based on Riley, 1990b; Waters et al., 2009). The Bowland High Group, the Craven Group, and the Millstone Grit Group formations (Pendleton to Rossendale) follow BGS terminology. Besides the major unconformity at the base of the Hodder Mudstone Formation, there are three local unconformities: a) base of the Embsay Limestone and equivalents; b) base of the Twiston Sandstone; c) base of the Pendleside Limestone Formation. MA = millions of years ago (dates after Davydov et al., 2010).

For the next 60 million years until the end of the Carboniferous Period, Gondwana steadily drifted northwards eventually colliding with Laurussia to form one supercontinent known as Pangea. This collision is marked by a mountain building episode known as the Variscan (Hercynian) Orogeny. This momentous event generated by powerful tectonic forces initially caused the continental crust where Great Britain lay to thin out (crustal extension) thus enabling marine basins to become established. Towards the end of the Carboniferous Period, compressive forces generated by the collision resulted in the inversion and erosion of the basins.

Another critical factor in the formation of the various rock types in the Bowland Sub-Basin was the waxing and waning of the Gondwana Ice Cap at the South Pole (fig. 1). As the climate warmed up the ice would melt and sea level would rise (marine transgression). When the climate cooled, the ice cap would lock-up water and sea level would fall (marine regression). Geologists refer to this as glacio-eustatic changes in sea level.

Regional setting

It is worthwhile differentiating between the Craven Basin (Hudson, 1933) and the Bowland Sub-Basin (fig. 4). The Craven Basin, sometimes referred to as the Bowland Basin (Ramsbottom, 1974), covers a wide geographical area which extends into the east Irish Sea. Within the Craven Basin there are smaller sub-basins, namely the Lancaster Fells Sub-Basin and the Bowland Sub-Basin, both of which have their own distinctive geological histories.

The Bowland Sub-Basin is the focal point of this book. It is a northeast trending half-graben bounded to the south by the Pendle Fault, to the north by the faults of the Bowland Line (Arthurton et al., 1988), and to the northeast by the Craven Fault system. The sedimentary rocks deposited in the basin were folded and faulted during the Variscan Orogeny into a complex series of structures. Phillips (1836) introduced the term Ribblesdale Fold Belt to describe this series of northeast-southwest trending anticlines which are themselves cut by a series of northwest trending faults.

Marine sedimentation in the basin began on a shallow carbonate shelf or carbonate ramp which subsequently fractured and rifted into a series of intra-basin highs and lows. As the base of the sequence is unexposed, the

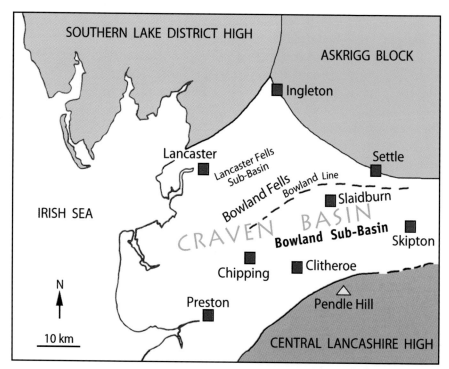

Fig. 4 The location of the Bowland Sub-Basin within the Craven Basin of northwest England. The Craven Basin extends westwards into the Irish Sea, and is defined by the Southern Lake District High, the Askrigg Block to the north, and the Central Lancashire High to the south. The Bowland Line separates the Lancaster Fells Sub-Basin from the Bowland Sub-Basin (after Riley 1990b).

age and nature of the oldest Carboniferous rocks are unknown, however, seismic evidence suggests that the fill of the basin is in the region of 6 km thick and consists of predominantly argillaceous carbonate rocks with lesser siltstones and sandstones.

Mudrocks and Limestones

The dominant rock types seen in the field are mudrocks and limestones. If identified correctly they can tell you a great deal about the environment in which they were deposited. 'Facies', a term often used alongside limestones and mudrocks, refers to the combined lithological and biological attributes of a sedimentary rock.

Mudrocks (shales and mudstones) contain far more information about their depositional history than is apparent from their supposedly uniform appearance. They can record evidence of salinity, oxygen levels, substrate type, and the environmental stability. Many mudrocks contain nodules formed most commonly of calcite, siderite and pyrite. Some of these nodules can contain uncompacted fossils such as ammonoids. Mudrocks deposited in environments with very little oxygen tend to be enriched in organic matter. Such organic-rich mudrocks (commonly called black shales or paper shales because of their appearance) are the source of most of the world's oil. A great deal of information can be retrieved by studying the contained fossils and sedimentary structures, information which requires little more than a hammer or a penknife to extract.

For a sedimentary rock to be called a limestone it should be composed dominantly of calcium carbonate, but where does this come from? The answer can be found in marine ecosystems which support a diverse community of corals and algae, around which organisms such as clams, oysters, snails (gastropods), and lampshells (brachiopods) live, and above which plankton float. Although they all look so different from one another, many share an important characteristic; they make solid shells of calcite (or sometimes aragonite). When these organisms die their skeletons accumulate on the sea bed and form limestone.

There are many different kinds of limestones, however, the two common types in the Bowland Sub-Basin are fossiliferous limestone (bioclastic) which consists of identifiable shells and shell fragments, and micrite which consists of lime mud. In order to identify different limestones in the field, a useful guide was devised by Dunham (1962) based on limestone texture. With a hand-lens it should be possible to identify Dunham's four principal types: calcareous mudstones, wackestones, packstones, and grainstones. Calcareous mudstones are rocks composed of greater than 75% mud-grade carbonate whereas wackestones (fig.5) are carbonate rocks containing less than 75% mud-grade carbonate (i.e., not quite as muddy as a mudstone!). Packstones (fig.6) on the other hand are grain supported with intergranular spaces filled with mud-grade carbonate (fragments of fossils such as crinoid ossicles may be visible). Grainstones (fig.7) are grain supported with little mud-grade carbonate in evidence and easily recognizable fossils. The 'grain' refers to skeletal fragments derived from fossils such as echinoderms and bryozoans.

Fig. 5   Wackestone from the Rain Gill Limestone, Slaidburn.

Fig. 6   Packstone from the Hetton Beck Limestone,
Sykes Quarry, Trough of Bowland.

Fig. 7   Grainstone from Salthill Quarry crinoidal biosparite bed.

Tournaisian Stage

Sedimentary rocks belonging to the Tournaisian Stage (Bowland High Group of Waters et al., 2009) are mainly limestones. The two formations which comprise this stage are the Chatburn Limestone which was deposited in an open marine platform environment, and the Clitheroe Limestone which was deposited in deeper water on a carbonate ramp. These two carbonate environments were relatively short-lived as they became submerged and buried beneath basinal mudstones in response to active rifting (Gawthorpe, 1987) and periodic eustatic sea level rises.

Chatburn Limestone Formation

The Chatburn Limestone (Parkinson, 1926) was defined as the Chatburn Limestone Group (Earp et al., 1961) and then redefined as a formation (Fewtrell & Smith, 1980). With a measured thickness of 838 m, this is the earliest known Carboniferous strata to be deposited in the basin. The formation comprises a marine sequence of shallow water limestones and fine terrigenous clastics. The limestones are generally well-bedded predominantly dark blue-grey packstones and grainstones, with frequent calcareous muddy partings. The Chatburn Limestone was deposited on a shallow carbonate shelf ranging from 75-100 m in water depth. The rate of sedimentation into the basin kept pace with subsidence, hence the seafloor remained at a relatively uniform depth.

At the western end of the Clitheroe Anticline, quarrying for Chatburn Limestone in Tarmac's quarry has recently ceased. Adjacent to this quarry is Castle Cement's Lane Head Quarry, now part of the Hanson Heidelberg Cement Group. Both quarries exhibit a number of interesting geological features such as faults, and a variety of folds including synclines, anticlines, and thrusts. (figs.8, 9, 10, 11, pages 17-18). It was during the 1961 survey that the Chatburn Limestone was informally defined successively into the Gisburn Cotes Beds, Horrocksford Beds, Bankfield East Beds and Bold Venture Beds (fig.3, p. 11). Since the Earp et al. (1961) memoir was published, these quarries have changed out of all recognition.

Within the Chatburn Limestone there are a few bedding planes with abundant fragmentary fossils. Solitary and colonial corals, brachiopods, gastropods and trilobites all adapted well in seas that remained well

Fig. 8   In the Chatburn Limestone the coral *Cyathoclisia tabernaculum* marks the top of the Horrocksford Beds in Lane Head Quarry, Clitheroe. Two pence coin for scale. Photo © Peter del Strother.

Fig. 9   Anticlines and synclines in the Bankfield East Beds, Chatburn Limestone, Lane Head Quarry, Clitheroe. The outcrop is about 5 m in height.

- 17 -

Fig. 10 Disturbed strata of the Bankfield East Beds indicate close proximity to the Horrocksford Hall Thrust Fault in Lane Head Quarry, Clitheroe.

Fig. 11 Bold Venture Tear Fault in Tarmac Quarry, Clitheroe. A small north-westerly trending tear fault which has offset the 'Four Foot Shale' and the anticlinal axis and the Horrocksford Hall Thrust to the south-south-east.

oxygenated. However, there is plenty of pyrite and evidence for low oxygen levels within the sediment. This was probably caused by high organic productivity. Although fossils as hand-specimens are rarely abundant, fragmentary bioclasts are visible with a hand-lens. There are plenty of trace fossils and the limestone is extensively bioturbated, so much so that the primary sedimentary fabric is more or less obscured. Microfossils are extremely abundant in the Chatburn Limestone. There is a significant proportion of green algae (the palaeoberesellids), and sponge spicules are so abundant in certain horizons that the rock should properly be called a spiculite. Chert is found associated with the spiculites.

In the Skipton and Broughton Anticlines the Haw Bank Limestone has been widely regarded as being equivalent of the Chatburn Limestone. More restricted outcrops of the Chatburn Limestone in the Hodder Valley are confined to the cores of the Slaidburn Anticline, and to a lesser extent, in the Whitewell Anticline and the Throstle Nest Anticline. Deposition of the Chatburn Limestone Formation terminated when subsidence of the basin floor began to outpace sedimentation, i.e., the sea became much deeper.

The Chatburn Limestone Formation is succeeded by the Clitheroe Limestone Formation. As the sea became deeper, 'reef limestones', now commonly referred to as Waulsortian mud-mounds (Lees & Miller, 1995) make their first appearance. What are Waulsortian mud-mounds and how do they differ from reef limestones?

Waulsortian mud-mounds

There are numerous steep-sided hills (knolls) in the Bowland Sub-Basin. These knolls (figs.12,13,p.21) are all composed of limestone and have proved popular with fossil collectors since the late nineteenth century. Geologists originally referred to them as either 'knoll-reefs' or 'reef limestones'. Tiddeman (1889) and Parkinson (1926) considered these knolls to be mound-like accumulations of biogenic material formed on a sinking sea bottom, or reef limestones. The geological map (fig. 2, p. 10) shows the distribution of limestone knolls with one group occupying the Ribble Valley in the east, and a second group confined to the Hodder Valley in the west. Further research on these limestone knolls concluded that they are composed of Waulsortian limestone. Where was this done and who was involved?

The term 'Waulsortian' was first used in 1863 to describe a particular assemblage of limestones in the Lower Carboniferous of Belgium. It was Arthur Vaughan (1916) who observed that knoll-reefs in the Clitheroe area had the same fossil content as the Waulsortian reefs he had also visited in Belgium. During the 1950s it became apparent that Waulsortian limestones lacked the rigid skeletal framework typical of many other ancient and modern reefs seen today. Rather than having a framework produced by living organisms, Waulsortian limestone is largely composed of carbonate lime mud or 'micrite' (Lees, 2006) thus bringing an end to notion of 'reef limestone'. More appropriate terms such as 'carbonate mudbank' and 'mud-mound' were introduced to describe these enigmatic structures.

The origin of the mud is still debated amongst carbonate sedimentologists. Currently it is thought that the lime mud is of microbial origin, being characteristically soft, but still retaining a gel-like cohesion which allowed steep depositional slopes to form e.g., Worsaw Knoll (fig.12) and Ashnott Knoll (fig.13). More information about the composition of the mud has been revealed under the microscope where it is seen to be made up of microcrystalline calcium carbonate or 'micrite' for short. As to where the mud came from to form the mound is still a contentious area. Did the mud form in situ (autochthonous) or does it have a detrital origin (allochthonous), or perhaps a combination of both! Whichever way the mud was formed, another question still remains as to how it was bound into a coherent mound that could withstand the rigours of a deep sea environment. Some geologists subscribe to the view that the mud-binding agent was cyanobacteria and dasycladacean algae. Skeletal debris of the animals that inhabited the mounds, such as sponges, echinoderms and bryozoans, probably had a part to play in stabilising and strengthening mud-mounds.

Another surprising feature of Waulsortian mud-mounds is that they appear to have formed at an appreciable water depth, perhaps as deep as 200 m or more, where sunlight barely penetrates. As there is no equivalent feature seen in modern oceans, the origin and formation of mud-mounds will continue to attract interest from geologists for the foreseeable future.

In 1972 Miller & Grayson, in describing the origin and structure of Clitheroe's reef limestones, introduced a terminology which is useful for general description of Waulsortian mud-mounds in the field. They referred

Fig. 12   Ribble Valley Waulsortian mud-mounds viewed from the northwest flank of Pendle Hill. The large knoll is Worsaw Hill, and the smaller one to the left is Warren Hill. Both hills are composed of Bellman Limestone. The farm at the foot of Worsaw Hill featured in the film *Whistle Down The Wind* in 1961.

Fig. 13   Ashnott Knoll is the pock-marked mound in the centre of the photograph. It is composed of Coplow Limestone and forms the core of a northeast trending anticline. The knoll was a bathymetric high in the Bowland Sub-Basin (fig. 19, p. 28) and therefore able to exert some control over sedimentation, particularly during deposition of the Hodder Mudstone Formation. Mining for galena (lead) on the knoll took place during the early 19th century. The line of sheep on the knoll provide the scale. Waddington Fell in the distance is capped by Pendle Grit.

to the white or grey, poorly bedded Waulsortian limestone i.e., the core of the mud-mound as 'bank beds' (fig.14). Each bank may consist of several stacked mounds which accumulated in a relatively low energy regime. Immediately surrounding the bank beds are 'flank beds' which consist of thick-bedded to flaggy crinoidal packstones and grainstones, commonly with depositional dips. These beds were deposited in a more turbulent environment as indicated by many disarticulated crinoid stems. The flank beds often pass laterally into more peripheral 'inter-bank beds' (fig.15) which generally consist of well-bedded, lenticular, crinoidal packstones with thin mudstone partings. These beds have a much more diverse assemblage of fossils than the flank beds. It is not unusual to find whole crinoid calyces preserved which suggests more tranquil conditions of deposition. Flank beds and inter-bank beds are not in themselves Waulsortian in character because such lithologies also occur where there are no Waulsortian mud-mounds.

Sedimentary strata is usually laid down horizontally in beds. If these beds become subjected to tectonic forces they may become tilted. Field geologists mapping the beds would then measure the amount of dip with a clinometer. In the case of Waulsortian mud-mounds the slopes are depositional as opposed to tectonic. In order to avoid misinterpretation in the field geologists might look for geopetals (also known as fossil spirit-levels) in the limestone. By analysing geopetals in the 1970's, Miller & Grayson noticed that depositional dips that occurred on Clitheroe's mud-mounds radiated away from the central core of the mound on all sides (also known as a quaquaversal dip). So what are geopetals and how do field geologists make use of them? Geopetals are the sediment infills of fossils. In Salthill Quarry (as with many other ancient reefs), cavities in shells or crinoid stems are ideal sediment traps for preserving these sedimentary features. When crinoids died and their skeletons disintegrated and sank to the sea bed, mud held in suspension sometimes settles out inside the central hole in the crinoid stem (or a shell) forming a layer of mud in the bottom. The top of the cavity may then be infilled by sparry calcite. If, subsequently, the rocks are eroded and / or tilted, the geopetal will record the horizontal of when the bed was initially formed. The brachiopod shell in Figure 16 is a good example of what to look out for. The top part shows the brachiopod fossil with part of the shell missing at the right hand side. The lower part is a view from the right side of the fossil where a perfect geopetal has formed. Sediment has settled in the bottom half of the cavity, whilst the top half has been filled with yellowish sparry calcite.

Fig. 14 Cross-section of a Waulsortian mud-mound in the Salthill Quarry. The paler coloured unbedded limestone is the micritic mud of the core of the mound. Miller & Grayson (1972) described the micrite core as bank beds. Inter-bank beds are the darker bedded limestone seen draping across the top of the mound. This is also Locality 1 of Bowden et al. 1997. Information board is 1 m tall for scale.

Fig. 15 Thinly bedded inter-bank limestone 1 m above the clipboard demonstrates rapid lateral facies change over 2 to 3 m by inter-tonguing with a cleaner crinoidal flank limestone. This is Locality 9 in the Salthill Quarry Trail of Bowden et al. 1997.

Scale ———— 4 cm ————

Fig. 16
Top: Pedicle (ventral) valve of a *Spirifer*.
Bottom: Cross-section through the *Spirifer* showing the geopetal cavity.
(Bellman Limestone Member)

The similarities and differences between ancient carbonate buildups and other reefs offer much scope for further discussion. Mud-mound origins remain one of the most complex areas of current debate in the general area of reef studies. These fascinating structures seen throughout the Bowland Sub-Basin should continue to attract future interest in years to come.

Clitheroe Limestone Formation

The transition from the Chatburn Limestone Formation into Clitheroe Limestone Formation (Riley, 1990b) is conformable, however, at the top of the Clitheroe Limestone there is major basin-wide unconformity between the Tournaisian Stage and the Viséan Stage (fig.3, p.11). The Clitheroe Limestone Formation includes in ascending order the following members: Thornton Limestone, Coplow Limestone, Peach Quarry Limestone and Bellman Limestone. The lithology of this formation generally consists of mainly pale grey, sometimes coarsely crinoidal packstones, wackestones, subordinate grainstones, and mudstones. Waulsortian mud-mounds occur at two levels i.e., in the Coplow Limestone Member and the Bellman Limestone Member. Whereas the Chatburn Limestone was deposited on a shallow-water carbonate shelf, deposition of Clitheroe Limestone took place in deeper water on a carbonate ramp. Progressive steepening of the ramp towards the south was a major factor in the Clitheroe Limestone being subjected to dramatic rapid lateral changes in thickness and facies. The buildup of Waulsortian mud-mounds was briefly interrupted by a phase of shallowing of the sea.

The first member of the Clitheroe Limestone Formation deposited on the shallower part of the carbonate ramp in the northern part of the basin is the **Thornton Limestone Member** (Hudson & Dunnington, 1944). At outcrop this limestone is commonly wavy-bedded, cherty, consisting of predominantly dark grey packstones and wackestones. It is not known for having a diverse fossil assemblage, although scattered brachiopods and coral colonies are not altogether uncommon.

Further south in the deeper part of the basin, shelf carbonates give way to Waulsortian limestones of the **Coplow Limestone Member**. This is a richly fossiliferous limestone being well known to fossil collectors for its abundance of corals, brachiopods, gastropods, bryozoans, trilobites and echinoderms. The name Coplow Limestone comes from Coplow Quarry, 1.8 km north-northeast of Clitheroe Castle. It is an important Waulsortian limestone locality and an internationally famous collecting ground for echinoderm fossils. Not surprisingly it is also a designated Site of Special Scientific Importance (SSSI). Unfortunately it has largely been covered over with quarry waste. The quarry owners recognise the scientific importance of Coplow Quarry and have taken steps to preserve some of the quarry faces for future scientific study.

There are good exposures of Coplow Limestone at Hall Hill, a disused quarry east of Whitewell, on the northern limb of the Cow Ark Anticline in the Hodder Valley. This locality was comprehensively described by Black (1954) and is one of the most impressive (and accessible) carbonate mud-mounds in the Bowland Sub-Basin. The diagnostic trilobite *Phillipsia gemmulifera* has been found here confirming Coplow Limestone age. By the old lime kiln there are 4 m of flank and inter-bank beds. In the main part of the quarry

Fig. 17 The south face of Hall Hill Quarry near Whitewell in the Hodder Valley. The yellow hard hat marks the base of a mud-mound, the pale unbedded micritic wackestone or bank beds of Miller & Grayson (1972). Thinly-bedded cherty packstones of flank and inter-bank beds outcrop below the yellow helmet.

north of the lime kiln these beds pass into Waulsortian limestones (fig.17). Crinoid calyces found at Hall Hill include *Actinocrinites* and *Gilbertsocrinus*. Joints and fissures are also a feature of this quarry together with conspicuous and well preserved laminated dolosilt (fig.18) that covers several joint planes. These tough veneers of dolosilt were probably formed by chemical modification of the limestone by magnesium rich solutions. Waulsortian mud-mounds of Coplow Limestone age are also seen in numerous isolated outcrops from Ashnott near Newton to the Thornley Anticline south of Chipping.

Fig. 18   Dolosilt from Hall Hill Quarry, Coplow Limestone.

Deposition of Coplow Limestone was terminated by a phase of shallowing of the sea. This change in water depth is recorded by deposition of the storm-generated **Peach Quarry Limestone Member** which is only exposed in the Clitheroe area. It is a lenticular unit and is restricted to the southern limb of the Clitheroe Anticline. Although 6 m are exposed in an abandoned tramway cutting close to Bellman Quarry, this limestone is better observed along the main A59 road-cutting between Clitheroe and Chatburn. The outcrop consists of 70 m of pale grey packstones and grainstones disposed in thin to thick multistory beds, sometimes wavy-bedded and cherty, with abundant crinoid, algal and pellet grains. Bedding planes crowded with brachiopods have been recorded from the A59 section. Miller and Grayson describe this section as black bituminous inter-bank facies with gradual upward transition through flank facies into typical bank facies of Crow Hill (Bellman Limestone Member) exposed 200 m further south towards the turn-off for the hamlet of Worston.

As the carbonate ramp began subsiding once more heralding a return to a deeper water environment, a second generation of mud-mound development occurred in the **Bellman Limestone Member**. This limestone is up to 800 m thick and consists of Waulsortian limestones with subordinate packstones, wackestones, and grainstones. In the Hodder Valley spectacular outcrops of Bellman Limestone are restricted to the northern limb of the Whitewell Anticline around Long Knots, west of the Inn At Whitewell. In the Ribble Valley there are numerous outcrops of Bellman Limestone from Twiston north of Pendle Hill to Clitheroe Castle in the centre of town.

Bellman Limestone has been extensively quarried by Castle Cement and is being actively worked in Bellman Quarry at the time writing. Salthill Quarry on the other-hand is a disused quarry and a designated SSSI. The Bellman

Limestone Member is equivalent to the 'Salthill Bank Beds' of Miller and Grayson (1972). The top of the mud-mound in Salthill Quarry (fig.14) marks the approximate stratigraphical position of the major unconformity at the Tournaisian/Viséan boundary. This unconformity is associated with sea level fall and oceanographic changes on a global scale. Geologists are using microfossils such as foraminifera e.g., *Eoparastaffella simplex*, and conodonts, as well as gamma-ray spectrometry to investigate this interval. The termination of this final phase of Waulsortian limestone build-up coincides with basin-wide erosion and fragmentation of the carbonate ramp into a series of depositional lows and highs (fig.19). This resulted in a complete reorganisation of depositional style during the Viséan stage.

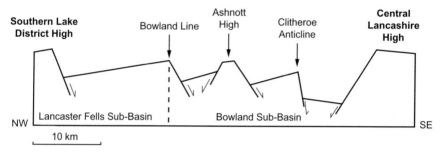

Fig. 19 Schematic cross-section of the Craven Basin during the Viséan (after Riley, 1990b). The Bowland Line separates the Lancaster Fells Sub-Basin to the NW from the Bowland Sub-Basin to the SE. Note that the Bowland Sub-Basin has been fractured into a series of fault bounded highs and bathymetric lows.

Viséan Stage

Viséan strata consists of four formations. In ascending order they are the Hodder Mudstone, Hodderense Limestone, Pendleside Limestone and Bowland Shale. The thickness of Viséan strata in the basin is around 900 m. Collectively these formations make up the recently introduced Craven Group (Waters et al., 2009). Viséan sedimentary rocks accumulated primarily from suspension in moderately deep water usually below storm wave base. The depositional lows were initially infilled with limestone boulder beds, packstones and grainstones, as a result of submarine erosion during the break-up of the carbonate ramp. This was followed by frequent influxes into the basin by skeletal carbonates (turbidites) from the highs and the surrounding shelves and platforms. Relatively steep slopes are indicated by the presence of slumps, debris flows and gravity slides. As the basin continued to subside, thus becoming much deeper and more anoxic (depleted of oxygen), turbidite limestones were gradually replaced by hemipelagic mudstones. Some of the mudstone horizons developed marine bands during periods of high salinity. Increasing pulses of sand into the basin (Buckbanks, Twiston, Pendleside and Hind Sandstone) set the scene for another major change in depositional style, this time from advancing river deltas of the Millstone Grit Group.

Hodder Mudstone Formation

The Hodder Mudstone Formation was named by Riley (1990b) and takes its name after the type section on the River Hodder 1.8 km east-northeast of Doeford Bridge. This formation was previously referred to as the Worston Shales by Earp et al. (1961) and Fewtrell & Smith (1980). It consists of a monotonous sequence of predominantly mudstones and siltstones with subordinate detrital limestone and sandstone (fig.20). Limestone conglomerates and breccias are present near the base whilst soft-sediment slumping and gravity slides are more widespread throughout the sequence.

Fig.20 Gently dipping mudstones, siltstones and wackestones in Crag Beck, 0.5 km north-north-west of Ashnott Knoll near Newton. This outcrop illustrates marked alternations in depositional style between hemipelagic mudstones and turbiditic limestones. Hammer for scale.

Accurate chronostratigraphic dating of the Hodder Mudstone has largely been achieved with thick-shelled ammonoids (also known as goniatites). These are associated with thin hemipelagic marine bands developed during periods of marine transgression. In the early-to-mid Viséan, ammonoids are prolific throughout a variety of lithologies in a totally marine sequence. They provide the greatest biostratigraphical resolution because they rapidly evolved into new species, they were free swimmers, and their preservation as fossils occurred on a global stage (Bisat, 1924). The downside is they are often preserved in a crushed state making identification difficult. Marine bands still remain a reliable means of correlating Carboniferous strata.

The **Limekiln Wood Limestone Member** marks the base of the Hodder Mudstone Formation. It comprises detrital crinoidal limestones, limestone breccias and boulder beds, which are commonly seen banked up against and infilling the eroded relief of the Clitheroe Limestone Formation. Parkinson (1926) first recognised this member and mapped it as the 'Thornley reef conglomerate' in Arbour Quarry on the south-eastern limb of the Thornley Anticline, 3 km south of Chipping (fig.21). The section extends for about 200 m along the south face, although much of it is overgrown. In the

Fig. 21   Limekiln Wood Limestone boulder bed in disused Arbour Quarry. Sub-rounded boulders of wackestone up to 0.5 m diameter were probably derived from Waulsortian limestone (Coplow age) exposed in the same quarry. Hammer for scale.

Clitheroe Anticline the Limekiln Wood Limestone was informally described as the 'Salthill Cap Beds' (Miller & Grayson, 1972). The type locality is the Plantation Farm Anticline 2 km east-northeast of Doeford Bridge where the Hodder river has cut a dramatic gorge through the sequence. Here the limestone reaches a thickness of up to 120 m, is repeatedly exposed in isoclinal and box folds, and is richly fossiliferous (fig.22). The packstones are commonly laminated with graded bedding and erosive bases (fig.23). Crinoidal debris and chert lenses are also conspicuous at the type locality.

Fig. 22 Limekiln Wood Limestone in the Plantation Farm Anticline. Fine- to coarse-grained packstone with abundant crinoid fragments. Two pence coin for scale.

Fig. 23 Fine- to coarse-grained packstone showing erosive feature on the base of the bed. The arrows point to where the coarse-grained crinoidal limestone is cutting down into finer-grained limestone. Two pence coin for scale.

The top of the Limekiln Wood Limestone is conformable with the overlying Phynis mudstones.

The **Phynis Mudstone Member** is typically a blocky, dark grey, finely micaceous calcareous mudstone, interbedded with laminated siltstones. It is equivalent to the Phynis Shales of Parkinson (1936) and was formally defined by Riley (1990b). In the southern half of the basin it attains a thickness of up to 350 m in the Plantation Farm Anticline, but elsewhere is usually less than 50 m thick. At the type locality of Phynis Beck in Slaidburn it is richly fossiliferous. In Barn Gill southeast of Phynis Beck, the Phynis Mudstone is conformable with the overlying Whitemore Limestone.

The 80 m thick **Whitemore Limestone Member** is a turbidite limestone that was defined by Riley (1990b) at Whitemore Knot, in the Whitewell Anticline, west of Burholme Bridge. It also outcrops in Barn Gill in Slaidburn as a fine- to coarse-grained bioclastic packstone which has yielded a rich fauna including complete carapaces of the trilobite *Gitara* sp. and the ammonoids *Ammonellipsites* sp. and *Eonomismoceras* (Riley, 1982). The Whitemore Limestone was probably derived from the Hetton Beck Limestone which was being deposited on the carbonate ramp to the north.

The **Hetton Beck Limestone Member** was first recognised by Booker & Hudson (1926) and described by Arthurton et al. (1988) prior to being formally defined by Riley (1990b). The type locality is situated southwest of Rylstone in the northern part of the basin. This limestone turbidite unit is 130 m thick and is primarily composed of packstones, wackestones and floatstones. A large disused quarry exposes up to 85 m of Hetton Beck Limestone (fig.24) in the core of Sykes Anticline on either side of the Trough Road, Sykes in Bowland, near the waterworks. Discrete chert horizons and extensive silicification are common features of this limestone. Selective silicification and weathering is indicated by the numerous well preserved *Syringopora* coral colonies (fig. 25), most of which appear not to be preserved in growth position. Fossils including disarticulated crinoids, bryozoans, brachiopods, solitary rugose corals and ammonoids are abundant at certain horizons. Gawthorpe & Clemmy (1985) recognised soft-sediment slumps and gravity slides at both West Sykes and East Sykes quarry. Another intriguing feature of Sykes quarry relates to the history of metaliferous ore mining first described by Raistrick (1973) and then Gill (1987). Both

Fig. 24 Hetton Beck Limestone in disused West Sykes Quarry, Trough of Bowland. The exploratory mining adits are visible towards the top of the section. Galena, baryte and fluorite can be collected from the extensive scree.

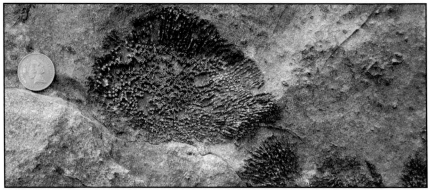

Fig. 25 Silicified *Syringopora* coral colonies weathered out of the Hetton Beck Limestone in West Sykes Quarry. Two pence for scale.

galena and sphalerite (zinc blende) have been intermittently extracted from the core of the Sykes Anticline since the 16th century. Adits on both east and west sides of Losterdale Brook testify to the existence of the former workings. Mineralisation at Sykes (and throughout the Ribblesdale Fold Belt) is probably associated with the expulsion of fluids from the hemipelagic mudstones during deep burial whilst under tectonic stress at the onset of the Variscan Orogeny.

The 50 m thick **Leagram Mudstone Member** (fig.26) marks a return to deep water calcareous shale. The type locality for this mudstone is Leagram Brook 2 km northeast of Chipping Parish Church. This unit was defined by Riley (1990b) and is equivalent to the Prolecanites compressus beds of Parkinson (1926). The dark grey, blocky, calcareous mudstone is interbedded with wackestone turbidites, and is exposed on the east bank of Leagram Brook in a prominent 5 m high meander cliff section. The ammonoid *Merocanites* has been found at this locality.

In Leagram Brook the outcrop of the **Buckbanks Sandstone Member** records an early entry of terrigenous sand into the basin, probably sourced from the Lake District High. The sandstone was defined and named by Riley (1990b) after Buckbanks Barn in Leagram Brook. The sandstone bed outcrops downstream of the Leagram Mudstone type locality in a tight syncline near the aqueduct. It is a 4 m thick bed of dark grey, brown, medium-grained, calcareous, bioclastic (crinoids and brachiopod debris) sandstone, interbedded with laminated mudstones and siltstones.

Fig. 26 The Leagram Mudstone exposed in the meander cliff in Leagram Brook is a blocky, pyritic and calcareous mudstone interbedded with thin dark wackestones. Crushed conches of the ammonoid *Merocanites* have been found on bedding planes. A4 clipboard for scale.

The following three limestone units are all similar in age and tend to dominate in different parts of the basin. Geologists use the term coeval to describe strata known to have close chronostratigraphic ages.

The **Embsay Limestone Member** (fig.27) was first mapped by Hudson & Mitchell (1937). It is confined to the eastern part of the basin outcropping in the Lothersdale and Skipton Anticlines. It is considered partly coeval with the succeeding Rain Gill Limestone and Chaigley Limestone from the

Fig.27 Gently dipping pale coloured Embsay Limestone in Raygill Quarry, Lothersdale. The white colouration is predominantly barytes mineralisation. Embsay Limestone was first mapped by Earp et al. 1961 as Chatburn Limestone. Earlier it was referred to as the 'Main Limestone' by Bray (1927). The 1 m post with attached yellow life belt provides scale.

western part of the basin. The Embsay Limestone turbidite is up to 100 m thick and consists of pale packstones and grainstones with interbedded hemipelagic calcareous silty mudstones. The source of the detrital carbonate is the surrounding shelf limestones which were gravitationally fed into this part of the basin. In Raygill Quarry the Embsay Limestone is exposed in the core of the Lothersdale Anticline, and the adjacent disused Dowshaw Delf Quarry 2 to 3 km west-southwest of Lothersdale Church. Fossils are not common at either locality. Faulting in the quarry also reveals mineral workings for baryte with some calcite and fluorspar. Mining for baryte in Raygill Quarry ceased in 1895.

The **Rain Gill Limestone Member** (fig. 28) was first described as the Middop Limestone in the Middop Anticline (Earp et al., 1961) between Pendle Hill and Weets Hill, near Barnoldswick. Arthurton et al., 1988 named the same limestone in the Slaidburn Anticline as the Rain Gill Limestone. This was subsequently formally defined and extended geographically by Riley (1990b) to include outcrops in the Ashnott and Whitewell Anticlines. The unit consists of thin- to thick-bedded wackestones and subordinate packstones, dark grey, fine- to coarse-grained, usually cherty and muddy. The top and bottom of the member are unexposed at the type locality. Slump folds are common here, and at other exposures in the Bowland Sub-Basin. The 170 m thick Rain Gill Limestone is sourced in similar fashion to the Embsay Limestone i.e., from the surrounding carbonate shelf.

Fig. 28   Rain Gill Limestone in a disused quarry 0.5 km southwest of Rain Gill. The wackestones and packstones are gently dipping and well-bedded. Slump folds are a feature of this quarry. Hammer for scale.

The **Chaigley Limestone Member** (fig.29) was named and formally defined by Riley (1990b) taking the name from the hamlet of Chaigley. The type locality is along the north bank of the River Hodder at Paper Mill Wood where the limestone appears to be much coarser and bioclastic than the previous two limestone members described. Ripples and slump folds are common as are soft-sediment depositional structures. Within the 180 m thick Chaigley Limestone there is a 30 cm thick dark calcareous mudstone known as the Dunbarella Bed. This bed is crowded with the bivalves *Dunbarella* and *Pteronites*. The type section for this bed is in the banks of Bonstone Brook, 0.6 km north-northwest of Ashnott Knoll near Newton.

Fig. 29 Variation in the Chaigley Limestone at the bottom of Agden Clough in the bedrock of the River Hodder. TOP: the limestone is coarsely bioclastic. (Two pence for scale) BOTTOM: the limestone is finely laminated. The lack of bioturbation suggests deposition in a dysaerobic/anoxic environment. (Camera case is 10 cm wide).

The top of the Hodder Mudstone Formation is marked by a second influx of terrigenous sand into the basin, this time from the **Twiston Sandstone Member** after the hamlet of Twiston near Clitheroe. It is a 4 m thick siliceous, calcareous and bioclastic, medium-grained sandstone. Earp et al. (1961) mapped this bed in the Lothersdale Anticline, but it was not named and formally defined until Riley (1990b). It outcrops in Dowshaw Delf Quarry in Lothersdale where it rests unconformably on Embsay Limestone.

Hodderense Limestone Formation

This is a pelagic limestone which derives its name from the ammonoid *Bollandoceras hodderense* (Bisat). It was first mapped informally by Parkinson in 1926 as the 'Beyrichoceras hodderense Bed'. Parkinson (1935) also mapped the bed between Pendle Hill and Middop. Prior to Parkinson, the Hodderense Limestone (fig.30) had been described by Hind & Howe in 1901 as being *a peculiar rock, greenish brown on weathered surfaces, but blue on fresh surfaces, blotched with purple and grey patches, very hard and compact and exhibiting a tendency to conchoidal fracture.* The type locality for this deep water marine limestone is the east bank of the River Hodder, Great Falls, near Stonyhurst College. The benthic fauna represents a community adapted to low oxygen levels (dysaerobic), with free-swimming and floating faunas being the most conspicuous. The Hodderense Limestone is usually a pale olive and blue-grey to cream coloured porcellanous wackestone and floatstone. Particularly good sections up to 10 m thick occur in numerous tributaries along the flanks of Pendle Hill, Easington Fell and Newton Fell.

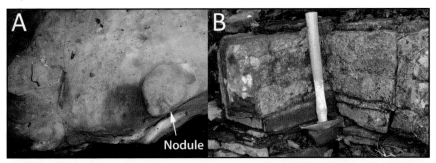

Fig. 30 The pelagic Hodderense Limestone Formation from two separate localities. **A** Hodderense Limestone with a nodule that may be a goniatite (25 mm). (Photo Smelfthwaites near Newton © Alan Whalley, 2009). **B** Hodderense Limestone in Rad Brook along the flanks of Pendle Hill. The fine-grained, blue grey, slightly blotchy nature of the limestone is evident on the fresh surface.

Pendleside Limestone Formation

The last major widespread limestone turbidite to enter the basin from the surrounding platform is the Pendleside Limestone (fig. 31 and fig. 32). It was recognised by Parkinson (1926), Earp et al. (1961), and formally defined by Riley (1990b). At the type locality in Burst Clough near Angram Green Farm on the lower flanks of Pendle Hill, a near complete section is exposed. Up to 300 m thick, the limestone is predominantly composed of fine- to coarse-grained packstones which are frequently bioturbated, occasionally cherty in character, and sometimes dolomitised. The bioturbation is reflected in the mottled appearance of the packstones. Towards the top of the sequence the limestone displays colour changes from pale olive to black, marking the transition into the foetid and petroliferous Bowland Shale Formation. The Pendleside Limestone is sometimes conglomeratic, being initially referred to as the 'Slaidburn Breccia' by Parkinson (1964). This conglomerate is equivalent to the sedimentary breccia recognised by Tiddeman (1891) in the Draughton Limestone on the Skipton Anticline. This was later referred to as 'Tiddeman's Breccia', a widely recognised marker bed (see Hudson & Mitchell, 1937) which is very well exposed in Hambleton Quarry near Skipton.

Metcalfe (1981) applied the term Rad Brook Beds to shaly beds low in the Pendleside Limestone Formation. Rad Brook is another stream section on the flanks of Pendle Hill, and is where Riley (1990b) formally defined the **Rad Brook Mudstone Member**. The base is defined at the first mudstone above the Hodderense Limestone Formation. These mudstones are dark olive to grey, calcareous and bioturbated, interbedded with siltstones, packstones and wackestones. The beds are absent north of Clitheroe and Whitewell. In the Ashnott Anticline near Newton, the Rad Brook Mudstone is only 60 cm thick and locally replaces the limestone. The Rad Brook Mudstone contains similar faunal groups to the Hodder Mudstone and the Hodderense Limestone Formations. Silicification and replacement by chert suggests the continuation of a marine environment where oxygen levels appear to be restricted. Hind (1907) collected the graptolite *Callograptus carboniferus* from Hook Cliff, which on further investigation turned out to be Rad Brook. Since then, Chapman et al. (1993) have revisited Rad Brook and defined the Pendle Dendroid Bed in the lowest part of the Rad Brook Mudstones. The graptolites are well preserved, occurring as flattened carbonised films, and in three-dimensions due to being infilled with pyrite.

Fig. 31 Steeply dipping and well-bedded Pendleside Limestone exposed in Hawshaw Slack Delf, Lothersdale anticline. A slump is evident where the hammer stands. This limestone varies throughout the basin e.g., conglomeratic at Clints Rock Quarry, Rylstone, and a breccia in Hambleton Quarry near Skipton.

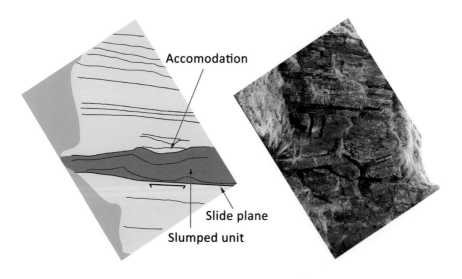

Fig. 32 An illustration of the main features of the slumped unit in the Pendleside Limestone (annotation by Ian Kane).

Bowland Shale Formation

The Bowland Shale Formation (Bisat, 1928) includes the Ravensholme Limestone, Park Style Limestone, Pendleside Sandstone, and the Hind Sandstone. The original Bowland Shale Group (Earp et al., 1961) was originally subdivided into Lower and Upper Bowland Shale Formations. The British Geological Survey propose to treat both formations as one unit due to the fact that there is no clear lithological change across the boundary at the base of the Cravenoceras leion marine band.

The dark organic-rich calcareous mudstones of the Bowland Shale contains variable amounts of sandstone, limestone and limestone breccias, and is very fossiliferous towards the base (fig. 33). The shales and mudstones accumulated as hemipelagic deposits, in moderately deep water, mainly below storm wave base in oxygen-poor conditions. For much of the time the water was fresh or brackish. During periods of higher salinity, when connections to the

Fig. 33   Marine fossils in the Bowland Shale at Langcliff Cross Brook, Slaidburn. **A**: *Posidonia becheri* (a bivalve); **B**: Goniatite; **C**: *Posidoniella* (a bivalve). Two pence for scale.

nearby oceans were established, numerous marine bands were developed. By contrast the thin limestones and sandstones were fed into the basin during storms as limestone turbidites and siliciclastic sediments from the palaeo-coastline, and active deltas adjacent to the basin. Good preservation of fossils is characteristic of the Bowland Shale, especially where nodular wackestone 'bullions' occur. These nodules commonly preserve fossils in an uncrushed state making identification easier. Autochthonous benthic (bottom-dwelling) faunas such as bivalves tend to dominate these shales.

Little Mearley Clough on the flanks of Pendle Hill is the reference section for the Bowland Shale Formation. Along the Bowland Fells escarpment deposits of shale reach between 185 m and 225 m thick. In Ashnott near Newton there are approximately 90 m of shale. In Crimpton Brook on Marl Hill Moor the Bowland Shale (fig. 34) consists of blocky fissile mudstones, thinly intercalated, pyritic, and ferrugineous in places. The only marine band recorded is that of *Tumulites pseudobilinguis* (formerly *Eumorphoceras pseudobilingue*). There is also a Sulphur Spa (fig. 34, inset) situated in marshy

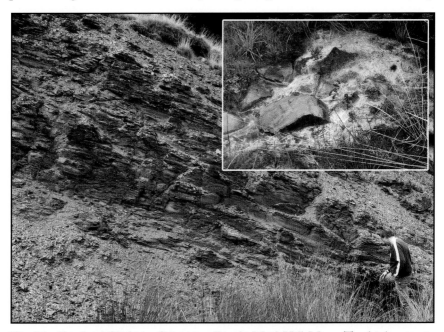

Fig. 34 Bowland Shale in Crimpton Brook, Marl Hill Moor. The high organic foetid shales are ideal source rocks for hydrocarbons. The Crimpton Pit Sulphur Spa nearby illustrates the high organic nature of the shales. (Inset: Scale 1 m diagonal)

ground between the shale outcrop and the road. Larger Sulphur Spars in the past have previously been used for medicinal purposes as they were thought to be a cure for leprosy.

Although discrete thin limestone turbidites are generally scattered throughout the Bowland Shale Formation, the two most prominent units are the Park Style Limestone and the Ravensholme Limestone. The type locality for the Park Style Limestone (Aitkenhead et al., 1992) is Leagram Brook where the entire 84 m thickness is exposed. The limestone is composed of an alternation of packstones, wackestones and interbedded mudstones. The calcareous dark grey mudstones are strongly bioturbated. The packstones are generally dark blue-grey, medium- to coarse-grained and bioclastic in parts, fining upwards into argillaceous wackestones. The lower division is approximately coeval with the Ravensholme Limestone seen in the Clitheroe area.

The Ravensholme Limestone was first named in the type area of the Clitheroe district (Earp et al., 1961). It is coarsely bioclastic and dominantly crinoidal and conglomeratic in places. It was deposited in the basin from the surrounding platform and basinal highs as turbidity currents and debris flows. Nearly the entire 35 m thickness of this limestone is exposed in Red Syke, a stream section east of Ravens Holme on the lower flank of Pendle Hill. There is also 16.5 m of Ravensholme Limestone exposed in Ram's Clough near Sykes Quarry in the Trough of Bowland. Here the limestone is represented by interbedded shaly mudstones and grainstones, and a large debris flow up to about 1 m in thickness.

The Ravensholme and Park Style Limestones are succeeded by the Pendleside Sandstone (fig.35), a thin sandstone-shale sequence best exposed on the lower flanks of Pendle Hill. This sandstone was formally referred to as the Pendleside Grit by Tiddeman, then renamed the Pendleside Sandstone by Parkinson (1935), and now Pendleside Sandstone Member by Aitkenhead et al. (1992). Good exposure occurs in Little Mearley Clough, Red Syke, Pendle Hill Brook, and near Lower Core Farm, Chipping. The sandstone turbidite comprises planar-bedded, fine- to medium-grained, grey brown sandstones, interbedded with shaly mudstone and siltstone. Maximum thickness attains 300 m and it crops out widely, though discontinuously, throughout the entire Bowland Sub-Basin. Some beds of the weakly calcareous sandstone may

Fig. 35 Pendleside Sandstone exposed in a roadside quarry near Lower Core Farm. The sandstone is fine-grained, weakly calcareous, and planar-bedded with shaly intercalations. Hammer for scale.

contain fragmentary bioclasts, particularly crinoid ossicles. Carbonaceous fragments and mudstone rip-up clasts are also common throughout.

In the upper part of the Bowland Shale Formation another intriguing sandstone was deposited into the basin. This was the Hind Sandstone which was first mapped and named by Moseley (1962). It outcrops between the Tumulites pseudobilingue and Cravenoceras malhamense marine bands. Although similar in character to the Pendleside Sandstone, the Hind Sandstone was subjected to soft-sediment deformation.

Both the Pendleside Sandstone and the Hind Sandstone are the main precursors to the arrival of the Pendle Grit, the oldest of the major Millstone Grit Group sandstones (fig.3, p.11). So once again the depositional style within the basin is about to be reshaped, this time by the advancing Pendle Grit deltas. The role played by the Hind Sandstone and the Pendle Grit is discussed fully in Chapter 4 by Ian Kane.

Glossary

algae — primitive plants including sea-weeds and plant plankton.

allochthonous — formed or produced somewhere else other than its present place.

ammonoid — see goniatite.

anticline — strata folded into an arch shape ranging from (m) to (km), with older strata in the centre.

aragonite — a mineral identical in composition with calcite, but differing from it in its crystalline form and some of its physical characters.

argillaceous — silt- to clay-grade sediment or sedimentary rock.

autochthonous — formed or produced in the place where found.

barytes — the mineral barium sulphate, usually white, commonly tabular and noticeably heavy.

benthic — describes bottom-living organisms.

bioclastic — limestone composed of shells or skeletal fragments.

biostratigraphy — dating and correlating strata with fossils.

bioturbation — disturbance of unconsolidated sediment by burrowing or feeding organisms.

bivalves — a group of molluscs with two shells (e.g. cockles, mussels, oysters) that live either on or buried within the sediment. The majority are filter feeders although some are sediment eaters.

brachiopods — marine invertebrates with a bi-valved calcite shell. The plane of symmetry is perpendicular to the plane of opening of the valves.

breccia — a sedimentary rock composed of angular fragments derived from the physical breakdown of pre-existing rock which has been cemented together.

bryozoa — marine animal with a skeleton commonly composed of calcite arranged in a distinctive array of tubular or box-like chambers.

calcite — crystalline form of calcium carbonate, the main constituent of limestones, and the hard parts of many invertebrates.

chert — a fine-grained rock composed of the mineral silica.

clastic — rocks composed of grains, or clasts, derived from the physical breakdown of pre-existing rocks.

coeval — occurring or existing at the same time.

conformable — strata deposited in continuous succession.

conglomerate — a sedimentary rock composed of rounded and sub-rounded clasts (pebbles, cobbles, boulders) of pre-existing rock cemented together in a finer grained matrix.

coral — an anemone-like marine animal with a basal skeleton of calcium carbonate and which may be solitary or colonial.

diagenesis — the physical and chemical processes that convert sediment into rock.

dolomite — a carbonate of calcium and magnesium that sometimes replaces calcite in limestone. Can be white, yellow or brown.

dysaerobic — an oxygen-deficient marine setting making life stressful for many faunas.

eustasy — world-wide changes in sea-level.

facies — all characteristics of a sedimentary rock that indicates its particular environment of deposition.

fault — a fracture in the strata where horizontal or vertical movement has taken place.

floatstone — a carbonate rock containing a few bioclasts or other fragments more than 2 mm in diameter, widely spaced, and embedded in sand- or mud-size carbonate matrix that forms over 90% of a rock.

fold — a bend or flexure in the bedded rock formed by plastic deformation.

foraminifera — microscopic single-celled animal with a chambered skeleton commonly composed of carbonate.

fossil — the preserved remains or traces of animals, plants, and other organisms from the ancient past.

geopetal —a rock fabric or structure that indicates the gravitational orientation of the rock at the time of deposition.

Gondwana — an ancient super-continent in the southern hemisphere, composed of South America, Africa, India, Madagascar, Australasia and Antarctica.

goniatite — Palaeozoic, free-swimming mollusc with a coiled, chambered shell, and related to extant cephalopods such as octopus.

hemipelagic — dominantly dark grey-black mudstones, occasionally calcareous with calcareous nodules (bullions), and usually deposited in a quiet and deep basinal environment.

Hercynian Orogeny — see Variscan Orogeny.

Laurussia — an ancient super-continent in the northern hemisphere, consisting of North America, Europe and much of Asia.

lithification — process of turning sediment into stone. Important influences are compaction and cementation.

lithology — the general character of a rock.

matrix — the smaller grains or cement of a sedimentary rock which infill the space between and bind together the larger clasts e.g., pebbles or shells.

micrite — microcrystalline calcite usually less than 5 Fm in grain size, found as matrix in many limestones.

orogeny — a mountain building event.

palaeoberesellids — benthic microfossils preserved as perforated calcareous tubes.

pelagic — marine animals living in the body of water, either floating (planktonic) or swimming (nektonic).

Permian — a period of geological time in which much of Britain was subjected to desert-like conditions (290 - 250 million years ago).

silicified — rock which has been replaced by silica. Commonly results in limestones being altered to chert.

stratigraphy — the description, correlation, and classification of strata in sedimentary rocks, including the interpretation of the depositional environments of those strata.

syncline — trough-shaped fold, ranging from (m) to (km), with youngest strata in the centre.

syndeposition — geological processes that occurred during deposition.

syntectonic — geological process or event occurring during any kind of tectonic activity

tectonic — relating to movement of rocks.

trace fossils — various activities of animals recorded in the sediment such as burrows, trackways and borings.

transgression — advance of sea over the land caused by a relative rise in sea level.

trilobite — an extinct group of marine arthropods.

turbidite — rock deposited from turbidity current, a submarine mass flow, usually fast flowing and highly charged with sediment, often poorly sorted and may show graded bedding.

unconformity — the junction between strata where sedimentation has not been continuous, and tectonic movements succeeded by erosion have produced a disjunction of bedding orientations between older and younger beds.

Variscan Orogeny — a mountain building episode caused by the collision of Gondwana and Laurussia

Acknowledgements
The following are thanked for their valuable comments, reviews or contributions: Dr. Stephen K. Donovan (Netherlands Centre for Biodiversity- Naturalis, Leiden, The Netherlands), Dr. Nick Riley MBE (British Geological Survey, Keyworth), Professor Paul Wignall (University of Leeds), Dr. Dave Bond (University of Leeds), Dr. Colin Waters (British Geological Survey, Keyworth), Jeremy J. Savill (CPGS), David Nelson (CPGS), Alan Whalley (CPGS), Peter del Strother MBE (PJDS Consulting), William Hudson (Austin, Texas, USA), Dr. Ron Blakey (Northern Arizona University, USA). and John Cordingley (Cave Diving Group).

References
Aitkenhead, N., Bridge, D. McC., Riley, N. J. & Kimbell, S. F. (1992): Geology of the country around Garstang. *British Geological Survey Memoir, England and Wales, Sheet 67.*

Arthurton, R. S., Johnson, E. W. & Mundy, D. J. C. (1988): Geology of the country around Settle. *British Geological Survey Memoir, England and Wales, Sheet 60.*

Baldwin, S. A. (2004): W. S. Bisat (1886-1973): his life and influence on Carboniferous stratigraphy. *Proceedings of the Geologists' Association, Vol. 11, pp. 371-377*

Bisat, W. S. (1924): The Carboniferous goniatites of the north of England and their zones. *Proceedings of the Yorkshire Geological Society, Vol. 20, pp. 40-124.*

Bisat, W. S. (1928): The Carboniferous goniatite zones of England and their continental equivalents. *Congrès pour l'Avancement des Etudes de Stratigraphie Carbonifère, Compte Rendu, Heerlen 1927*, 117-133.

Black, W. W. (1954): Diagnostic characters of Lower Carboniferous knoll-reefs in the north of England. *Transactions of the Leeds geological Association, Vol. 6, pp. 262-297.*

Booker, K. M. & Hudson, R. G. S. (1926): The Carboniferous sequence of the Craven Lowlands south of the reef limestones of Cracoe. *Proceedings of the Yorkshire Geological Society, Vol. 22, pp. 280-309.*

Bowden, A., Webster, M. & Mitcham, T. 1997. Salthill Quarry Geology Trail. *Geologists' Association Guide, 58, 30 pp.*

Chapman, A. J., Rickards, R. B. & Grayson, R. F. (1993): The Carboniferous graptolites of Britain and Ireland. *Proceedings of the Yorkshire Geological Society, Vol. 49, pp. 295-319.*

Conybeare, W. D. & Phillips, W. (1822): Outline of the geology of England and Wales. *Part 1. London.*

Cordingley, J. (2010): www.cavedivinggroup.org.uk/images/Photos/JNC/Malham/index.htm

Davydov, V. I., Crowley, J. L., Schmitz, M. D. & Poletaev, V. I. (2010): High-precision U-Pb zircon age calibration of (he global Carboniferous lime scale and Milankovitch band cyclicity in the Donets Basin, eastern Ukraine. *Geochemistry, Geophysics, Geosystems, Vol. 11, No. 1.*

De Rance, C. E. (1873): On the Occurrence of Lead, Zinc and Iron Ores, in some Rocks of Carboniferous Age in the North-West of England. *Geological Magazine. Vol. 10, pp. 64-74.*

del Strother, P. (2008): History of Ribblesdale Cement. *Published by Castle Cement Limited, Clitheroe, Lancashire BB7 4QF. ISBN 978-0-9545416-1-3*

Dunham, R. J. (1962): Classification of carbonate rocks according to depositional texture. *Memoir American Association of Petroleum Geologists, No. 1, pp. 108-121.*

Fewtrell, M. D. & Smith, D. G. (1980): Revision of the Dinantian stratigraphy of the Craven Basin, N. England. *Geological Magazine 117, pp. 37-49.*

Earp, J. R., Magraw, D., Poole, E. G. Land, D. H., & Whiteman, A. J. (1961): Geology of the country around Clitheroe and Nelson. *Memoir of the Geological Survey of Great Britain, Sheet 68 (England and Wales).* (London: HMSO).

Garwood, E. J. & Goodyear, E. (1924): The Lower Carboniferous succession in the Settle district and along the line of the Craven faults. *Quarterly Journal of the Geological Society, London, Vol. 80 pp. 184-273.*

Gawthorpe, R. L. (1987): Tectono-sedimentary evolution of the Bowland Basin, N. England, during the Dinantian. *Journal of the Geological Society (London) 144, pp. 44-59.*

Gawthorpe, R. L. & Clemmy, H. (1985): Geometry of submarine slides in the Bowland basin (Dinantian) and their relation to debris flows. *Journal of the Geological Society (London) 142, pp. 555-565.*

Greenhalgh, M. (2008): Ribble, River and Valley: a local and natural history. *Carnegie Publishing. ISBN 978-1-85936-135-1*

Gill, M. C. (1987): The Yorkshire and Lancashire lead mines: a study of lead mining in the south Craven and Rossendale districts. Northern Mines Research *British Mining No. 33.*

Harvey, A. M. (1985): The river systems of northwest England. *In: Johnson, R.H. (Ed.), The Geomorphology of northwest England. Manchester University Press, Manchester, pp. 122-142.*

Harvey, A. M. (1997a): Fluvial geomorphology of north-west England. northwest England. *In: Gregory, K.J. (Ed.), Fluvial geomorphology of Great Britain. Joint Nature Conservation Committee, Chapman and Hall, London, pp. 173-200*

Hind, W. (1907): On the occurrence of dendroid graptolites in British Carboniferous rocks. *Proceedings of the Yorkshire Geological Society, Vol. **16**, 155.*

Hind, W. (1918): On the Distribution of the British Carboniferous Goniatites, with a description of one New Genus and some New Species. *Geological Magazine, **6**, pp. 434-450.*

Hind, W. & Howe, J. A. (1901): The geological succession and palaeontology of the beds between the Millstone Grit and the Limestone-Massif at Pendle Hill and their equivalents in certain other parts of Britain. *Quarterly Journal of the Geological Society, London, **57**, pp. 347-402.*

Hudson, R. G. S. (1927): A mid-Avonian reef limestone and conglomerate in the Craven Lowlands. *Geological Magazine **64**, pp. 503-511.*

Hudson, R. G. S. (1933): The scenery and geology of north-west Yorkshire. *Proceedings of the then Geologists' Association, Vol. **44**, pp. 227-269.*

Hudson, R. G. S. & Dunnington. H. V. (1944): The Carboniferous rocks of the Swinden Anticline, Yorkshire. *Proceedings of the Geologists' Association, Vol. **55**, pp. 195-215.*

Hudson, R. G. S. & Mitchell, G. H. (1937): The Carboniferous geology of the Skipton Anticline. *Geological Survey of Great Britain, Summary of Progress for 1935, part **2**, pp. 1-45.*

Jones, R. M. (1908): George Fox An Autobiography. *www.jesus.org.uk/vault/library/fox_autobiog.pdf. Chapter VI, p. 62*

Lees, A. (2006): Waulsortian. In Dejonghe, L., ed., Current status of chronostratigraphic units named from Belgium and adjacent areas. *Geologica Belgica, Brussels, 9/1-2: pp. 151-155.*

Lees, A. & Miller, J. (1995): Waulsortian banks. In: Monty, C. L. V., Bosence, D. W. J., Bridges, P. H. & Pratt, B. R. eds. Carbonate Mud-Mounds, their Origin and Evolution. *International Association of Sedimentologists, Special Publication., 23, pp. 191-271.*

Metcalfe, I. (1981): Conodont zonation and correlation of the Dinantian and early Namurian strata of the Craven Lowlands of northern England. *Institute of Geological Sciences Report 80/10, pp. 1-70.*

Miller, J. & Grayson, R. F. (1972): Origin and structure of the Lower Viséan "reef" limestones near Clitheroe, Lancashire. *Proceedings of the Yorkshire Geological Society, Vol. 38, pp. 607-638.*

Moseley, E. (1962): The structure of the south-western part of the Sykes Anticline, Bowland, west Yorkshire. *Proceedings of the Yorkshire Geological Society, Vol. 33, pp. 287-314.*

Parkinson, D. (1926): The faunal succession in the Carboniferous Limestone and Bowland Shales at Clitheroe and Pendle Hill, Lancashire. *Quarterly Journal of the Geological Society, London, 82, pp. 188-249.*

Parkinson, D. (1935): The geology and topography of the limestone knolls in Bolland (Bowland), Lancs, and Yorks. *Proceedings of the Geologists' Association 46, pp. 97-120.*

Parkinson, D. (1936): The Carboniferous succession in the Slaidburn district, Yorkshire. *Quarterly Journal of the Geological Society, London, 92, pp. 294-331.*

Parkinson, D. (1964): The relationship of the Bowland shales to the Pendleside limestone in the Clitheroe, Slaidburn and Sykes Anticlines. *Geological Journal Vol. 4 pp. 157-166*

Phillips, J. (1836): Illustrations of the geology of Yorkshire. Part II, The Mountain Limestone District. *London: John Murray, 253 pp.*

Ramsbottom, W. H. C. (1974): Dinantian. *In* Raynor, D. H. & Hemmingway, J. E. (eds) The geology and mineral resources of Yorkshire. *Yorkshire Geological Society Occasional Publication, 2, pp. 47 - 73.*

Raistrick, A. (1973): Lead Mining in the Mid-Pennines. Truro: D. Bradford Barton Ltd.. p. 90.

Riley, N. J. (1982): Early Viséan trilobite and ammonoid faunas in the western part of the Craven basin. *Unpublished Ph.D. thesis, University of Bristol.*

Riley, N. J. (1990b): Stratigraphy of the Worston Shale Group (Dinantian) Craven Basin, north-west England. *Proceedings of the Yorkshire Geological Society, Vol. 48, pp. 163-187.*

Riley, N J. (1993): Dinantian (Lower Carboniferous) biostratigraphy and chronostratigraphy in the British Isles. *Journal of the Geological Society,London, Vol. 150, pp. 427-446.*

Vaughan, A. (1905): Palaeontological sequence in the Carboniferous limestone of the Bristol area. *Quarterly Journal of the Geological Society, London lxi, pp. 181-307*

Vaughan, A. (1916): The knoll region of Clitheroe, Bowland and Craven. *Proceedings of the Yorkshire Geological Society, Vol. xix, pp. 41-50.*

Waters, C. N., Waters, R. A., Barclay, W. J., & Davies, J. R. (2009): A lithostratigraphical framework for the Carboniferous successions of southern Great Britain (Onshore). *BGS Research Report, RR/09/01 194 pp.*

Winch, N. J. (1817): Observations on the geology of Northumberland and Durham. *Trans. Geological Society, London, Ser. 1, IV, 101 pp.*

Chapter 3

Fossil Echinoderms from the Mississippian (Lower Carboniferous) of the Clitheroe District

Stephen K. Donovan* & David N. Lewis+

*Department of Geology, Netherlands Centre for Biodiversity - Naturalis, Postbus 9517, NL-2300 RA Leiden, The Netherlands.
e-mail; Steve.Donovan@ncbnaturalis.nl
+ Department of Palaeontology, The Natural History Museum, Cromwell Road, London, SW7 5BD: e-mail; dnl@nhm.ac.uk

"... nowhere else in England have Carboniferous crinoids been found in such large numbers and also in such variety of genera and species [as around Clitheroe]" (Westhead, 1979, p. 465).

In the rock record of the British Isles, the greatest diversity of Echinoderms, the spiny skinned animals, is found in the Carboniferous, particularly the limestones of the Mississippian (Lower Carboniferous). The three commonest echinoderm groups in the Mississippian of the British Isles are the echinoids (sea urchins), blastoids (extinct) and, particularly, crinoids (sea lilies), whose remains may be present as hundreds of thousands of disarticulated elements, mainly columnals and pluricolumnals derived from the stem; only relatively few localities preserve crinoid cups and crowns. This interval is renowned for its rich crinoid faunas internationally and has been named the "Age of Crinoids" (see Kammer & Ausich, 2006).

Most of the specimens illustrated come from three notable localities in the Clitheroe area of Lancashire, namely Bellman, Coplow and Salthill quarries (Miller & Grayson, 1972; Grayson, 1981; Anon, 1983; Bowden et al., 1997). Despite the geographical focus of the present contribution, many of the genera considered herein have a wide distribution, and are known from mainland Europe, North America and elsewhere. We also discuss a few taxa for completeness that, although so far unknown from the Clitheroe area, are nevertheless typical of the Mississippian of the north of England.

We particularly draw attention to the Mississippian crinoids of western Yunnan, China, which unexpectedly share a number of species with Clitheroe (Webster et al., 2009, pp. 126-128, table 3): *Amphoracrinus atlas*? (M'Coy); *Amphoracrinus bollandensis*? Wright; *Amphoracrinus gilbertsoni*? (Phillips); *Cyathocrinites conicus*? (Phillips); and ?*Bollandocrinus erectus* Wright. Other genera similar between the two sites include *Gilbertsocrinus* Phillips, *Pimlicocrinus* Wright, *Platycrinites* Miller sensu stricto and *Synbathocrinus* Phillips.

The purpose of the present chapter is to provide an introduction to the echinoderm fauna of the Mississippian of the Clitheroe area, derived in part from two earlier guides by Donovan (1992) and Donovan et al. (2003); in particular, descriptions and photographs are reproduced from the latter. Detailed formal systematic descriptions of the echinoderms are available elsewhere (see references in text); herein, we aim to illustrate the principal genera, and discuss their morphology, preservation, occurrence, diversity and palaeoecology, as appropriate. Reference to a suitable undergraduate palaeontology textbook (such as Clarkson, 1998) and the Glossary (below) will enable the non-specialist to understand the specialist terminology used herein.

All of the specimens illustrated are deposited in the Department of Palaeontology, The Natural History Museum, London (BMNH). Descriptive terminology of the endoskeletons of crinoids, blastoids and echinoids follows Melville & Durham (1966), Beaver et al. (1967) and Moore & Teichert (1978). For detailed descriptions of most of the crinoid species mentioned herein, see Wright (1950-1960). All images, apart from Figures 1 and 2, are copyright of The Natural History Museum, London.

Fig. 1 James Wright

Two Noteworthy Amateur Palaeontologists

The Scotsman James Wright (1878-1957) (Fig. 1) spent his entire working life with the family linoleum and house-furnishing business in Kirkcaldy, Fife (Melville, 1958). He was encouraged by Dr. Francis A. Bather (1863-1934; Moore, 1978, pp.

T4-T5) of the British Museum (Natural History), London, to study the British Carboniferous crinoids. Wright's studies gave him an international reputation. His most enduring work is his comprehensive monograph of the British Carboniferous Crinoidea (1950-1960), published, in part, posthumously. Wright used to spend some of his holidays in Clitheroe (G.D. Sevastopulo, written comm. to S.K.D., May 2010), and many of his English specimens came from Coplow and Bellman quarries.

Stanley Westhead (1910-1986) (Fig. 2) was a notable amateur palaeontologist who was born and lived in Clitheroe, and collected the fossils of the local Carboniferous Limestone, particularly the echinoderms (Donovan, 1988). Stanley worked in the family textile business, served as a Major in the Royal Corps of Signals in World War Two and later served as a magistrate. Unlike James Wright, Stanley was content to accumulate and organise his specimens, and generously allowed others to research his collection. This is demonstrated nowhere better than Wright (1950-1960), in which four rare species are figured from the Westhead collection; three are type species and two are fittingly named *westheadi*. Specimens in the Westhead Collection (now in The Natural History Museum, London) formed the basis for the plates.

Fig. 2 Stanley Westhead

Systematic palaeontology
Class CRINOIDEA J. S. Miller, 1821

The stalked crinoids or sea lilies are an extant group of animals, but only found at water depths of 100+ m at the present day. In the Mississippian they also occur in deposits laid down in shallower water. As their name suggests, they have a plant-like appearance, but are animals related to starfishes and sea urchins. The skeleton of living and fossil crinoids is divided into an attachment structure (='root'); the column, a flexible stalk that elevates the crown; and the crown, which consists of the cup (containing the main organs of the body), tegmen (mainly a 'roof' on top of the cup) and arms, commonly branching, which gathered microscopic food particles that were pushed towards the mouth at the centre of the tegmen. Most illustrations are of the cup, with or without tegmen and arms, which are the parts of the crinoid principally used in classification. Features of the stem are discussed only in those instances where they are considered particularly diagnostic, such as platycrinitids and *Barycrinus*. Crinoids at Clitheroe rarely retain their free arms and these are discussed only where appropriate.

Subclass CAMERATA Wachsmuth & Springer, 1885
Order DIPLOBATHRIDA Moore & Laudon, 1943

Remarks. Dicyclic camerate crinoids with rigidly sutured cups, the proximal arms typically fixed and uniserial, and free arms pinnulate.

Gilbertsocrinus Phillips (Pl. 1, fig. A)

Description. Theca squat, subcylindrical. Infrabasal and basal circlets both comprised of five plates, hidden in basal concavity. Five hexagonal radials not in contact, with identical primanal in CD interray. Numerous interbrachial plates separating fixed arms. Tegmen low domed. Distinctive arm-like appendages of unknown function arose from the tegmen just above the position where the free arms are attached (not preserved in British specimens). Anal opening on tegmen. Fixed arms uniserial, branching once isotomously.

Remarks. *Gilbertsocrinus mammillaris* Phillips (Pl. 1, fig. A) is widespread in northwest England, including from Salthill Quarry. Other species from the Clitheroe area include *G. bollandensis* Wright and *G. coplowensis* Wright (both Coplow Quarry), *G. globosus* Wright (Salthill), and *G. konincki* Grenfell (Coplow and Salthill) (Donovan, 1992; Ausich & Kammer, 2006, appendix A).

Order MONOBATHRIDA Moore & Laudon, 1943

Remarks. Monocyclic camerate crinoids. The cup is rigidly sutured, the proximal arms typically fixed and uniserial, and free arms pinnulate.

Amphoracrinus Austin (Pl. 1, figs B, F)

Description. Theca subspherical to conical. Cup with three low, equal basals, five radials and a primanal in the radial circlet. Radials moderately high, hexagonal. Primanal heptagonal. Fixed arms uniserial, branching once isotomously, separated by a few large interbrachial plates. Anal tube eccentric and directed posteriorly. Four prominent oral plates in the apical position bear knob-like processes. Differs from *Actinocrinites* in having the anal tube positioned sub-apically and orientated posteriorly.

Remarks. Two species are illustrated, *Amphoracrinus turgidus* Wright (Bellman and Salthill quarries) and the type species *A. gilbertsoni* (Phillips) (Bellman, Coplow and Salthill quarries). Other nominal species from the Clitheroe area include *A. atlas* (M'Coy) (Bellman and Salthill), *A. bollandensis* Wright (Bellman, Coplow and Salthill), *A. compressus* Wright (Salthill) and *A. rotundus* Wright (Coplow). However, Wright 'over-split' the species of *Amphoracrinus* from the Clitheroe area; several of these species are junior synonyms (G.D. Sevastopulo, written comm. to S.K.D., May 2010).

Mcoycrinus Ausich & Kammer (Pl. 1, fig. G)

Description. Theca globular. Cup bowl-shaped, flattened, base flattened to depressed centrally. Three(?) basals support a circlet of five radials and a primanal in the radial circlet. Fixed arms uniserial, branching once isotomously, separated by a numerous interbrachials. Tegmen low domed, anal pyramid eccentric.

Remarks. *Mcoycrinus globosus* (Phillips) is the only species assigned to this genus from the British Isles. It occurs in northwest England (including Bellman and Salthill quarries), Derbyshire and possibly Lanarkshire.

Pimlicocrinus Wright (Pl. 1, fig. D)

Description. Close to *Amphoracrinus*, but with a low cup that may not be visible laterally; three low, equal basals in narrow circlet; tegmen high domed, with sub-central anal tube; and oral plates inconspicuous.

Remarks. The genus is named after the Pimlico area of Clitheroe. *Pimlicocrinus brevicalix* (Rofe) (Pl. 1, fig. D), precise locality unknown, is one of three nominal British species, best known from Clitheroe (Ausich & Kammer, 2006, appendices A, B). *Pimlicocrinus clitheroensis* (Wright) and *P. latus* Wright are found at Coplow Quarry.

Actinocrinites J. S. Miller (Pl. 1, figs E, I)

Description. Elongate, conical theca surmounted by a rigid, domed tegmen composed of numerous small plates. Three low, equal basals. Five elongate, hexagonal radials; elongate, pentagonal primanal in the radial circlet.

Fixed arms uniserial, branching once isotomously, separated by few large interbrachial plates and anal series. Tegminal plates may be spiny or tuberculated. Anal tube apical.

Remarks. Known from both Coplow and Salthill quarries, this genus is probably over-split and species such as the illustrated *Actinocrinites coplowensis* Wright await systematic revision (G.D. Sevastopulo, pers. comm. to S.K.D.). Donovan (1992, table 1) listed 14 species of *Actinocrinites* described from Coplow Quarry, twelve of which were erected by James Wright. Ausich & Kammer (2006, appendix A) recognised 16 species of this genus from Coplow Quarry, including four previously included in *Diatorocrinus* Wright, a junior synonym of *Actinocrinites*.

Thinocrinus Ausich & Sevastopulo (fig. 3)

Description. Close to *Actinocrinites*, but with relatively high basals and radials; the primibrachials form the highest part of the calyx walls along rays; and the 15-20 arms are grouped in lobes.

Remarks. The type species, *Thinocrinus westheadi* (Wright), was named by the prolific amateur James Wright in honour of his fellow collector and friend, Stanley Westhead of Clitheroe. See Ausich & Sevastopulo (2001, pp. 37-38, pl. 3, fig. 12, text-figs 9B-E, table 7) for a detailed discussion of this species.

Eumorphocrinus Wright (Pl. 1, fig. C)

Description. Conical to rounded theca surmounted by a rigid, domed tegmen composed of numerous small plates. Three low, equal basals. Five moderately high, hexagonal radials; primanal in the radial circlet. Fixed arms uniserial, branching once isotomously, separated by quite numerous interbrachial plates and anal series; first secundibrachials form part of the wall of theca. Tegminal plates numerous, low to moderately inflated. Anal tube apical, central.

Remarks. Eumorphocrinus excelsus Wright (Pl. 1, fig. C) is known from Coplow, Bellman and Salthill quarries (Ausich & Kammer, 2006, appendix A). *Eumorphocrinus erectus* Wright is known from Coplow Quarry only.

Platycrinites J. S. Miller (Pl. 2, figs B, C; fig. 4)

Description. (After Ausich & Kammer, 2006, p. 102.) "*Platycrinites* are platycrinitids lacking short ray lobes composed of fixed secundibrachials, five arm openings into the calyx, proximal brachials that are not fixed into the sides of the tegmen, the anus positioned on the tegmen upper surface or the upper edge of the tegmen, an anal tube present, few to numerous small- to medium-sized tegmen plates, a gradation of tegmen plates from larger orals to smaller tegmen plates at the abaxial margin of the tegmen, and free arms projecting upward or outward and upward."

Remarks. Thecae, cups and the distinctive columnals (Pl. 2, figs B, C) of *Platycrinites* are locally common particularly in the Lower Carboniferous of northern Europe and the U.S.A., assigned to hundreds of nominal species. Three nominal species are known from Coplow, one from Bellman and three from Salthill quarries (Ausich & Kammer, 2006, appendix A). The concept of the genus *Platycrinites* was recently clarified by Ausich & Kammer (2009).

Pleurocrinus Austin & Austin (Pl. 1, fig. H; Pl. 2, fig. F)
Description. (After Ausich & Kammer, 2006, p. 102.) "*Pleurocrinus* are platycrinitids with short ray lobes composed of fixed secundibrachials, ten arm openings into the calyx, proximal brachials that are not fixed into the side of the tegmen, the anus positioned onto the tegmen side or the upper edge of the tegmen, an anal tube absent, typically five (several species have more) medium- to large-sized tegmen plates, relative tegmen plate sizes either bimodal or with a gradation of tegmen plates from larger orals to smaller tegmen plates at the abaxial margin of the tegmen, and free arms projecting downward or outward and downward."

Remarks. Illustrated *Pleurocrinus coronatus* Goldfuss is one of at least 18 nominal species of *Platycrinites* + *Pleurocrinus* from the Clitheroe quarries, although they have been excessively split and require revision. So-called *Platycrinites* columnals (Pl. 2, figs B, C) may also be derived from *Pleurocrinus*. Four species of *Pleurocrinus* are common to both Bellman and Salthill quarries, namely *P. bellmanensis* (Wright), *P. coronatus* (Goldfuss) (Pl. 2, fig. F), *P. diadema* (M'Coy) and *P. pileatus* (Goldfuss); a fifth, *P. tuberculatus* (J.S. Miller), is a nomen dubium.

Brahmacrinus Sollas (Pl. 2, fig. A)
Description. Close to *Platycrinites*, but the proximal part of the arms is sutured to tegminal plates and the anal opening is sub-central (Pl. 2, fig. A). As with

Pleurocrinus, cups preserved without the tegmen are essentially similar to *Platycrinites* and similarities presumably exist between their columns.

Remarks. Brahmacrinus ponderosus Sollas (Pl. 2, fig. A) is the only British species and has a notably robust cup. It is known from both Coplow and Salthill quarries. It can be recognised from isolated radials that show a conspicuous U-shaped central depression (G.D. Sevastopulo, written comm. to S.K.D., May 2010).

Subclass CLADIDA Moore & Laudon, 1943
Remarks. Gracile to robust, apinnulate or pinnulate, dicyclic crinoids with none, one or more anal plates incorporated into the cup and a commonly prominent anal sac (Moore et al. 1978, p. T578). Arms commonly branched.

Primitive cladids
Remarks. Apinnulate cladid crinoids.

Barycrinus Meek & Worthen (Pl. 2, fig. H)
Description. Column pentameric, with weakly pentastellate axial canal and meric sutures apparent in lateral view. Cup large. Five low infrabasals, apparent laterally; five larger, hexagonal or heptagonal basals; square radianal in CD interray; five broad radials; pentagonal anal plate between C and D radials resting on radianal and posterior basal.

Remarks. The only nominal British species, *Barycrinus ribblesdalensis* (Wright), is probably from the Clitheroe area. The distinctive pluricolumnals of *Barycrinus* sp. are locally common at Salthill Quarry (Donovan & Veltkamp, 1990).

Cyathocrinites J. S. Miller (Pl. 2, fig. D)
Description. Cup bowl-shaped, with five low infrabasals, five pentagonal to hexagonal basals and five radials with narrow arm facets. Anal X supported by CD basal only and incorporated in radial circlet.

Remarks. Cyathocrinites planus J. S. Miller (Pl. 2, fig. D), the type species, is known from Coplow, Bellman and Salthill quarries. Ausich & Kammer (2006, appendix A) recognised a further six nominal species of *Cyathocrinites* from these quarries.

Advanced cladids
Remarks. Pinnulate cladid crinoids.

Poteriocrinites J. S. Miller (fig. 5)
Description. Cup conical, five pentagonal infrabasals and five hexagonal basals. Five radials wider than high, with C-shaped arm facets narrower than full width of plate and angled away from oral surface. Radials separated by anal series in CD interray. Radianal supports anal X and one other plate, all of which are incorporated in the cup. Arms long, uniserial, branching isotomously several times.

Remarks. This genus is common on both sides of the Atlantic. The type species, *Poteriocrinites crassus* J. S. Miller, is known from the three main Clitheroe quarries (Donovan, 1992).

Bollandocrinus Wright (Pl. 2, fig. E)
Description. Cup conical, five pentagonal infrabasals and five hexagonal basals. Five radials wider than high, with C-shaped arm facets narrower than full width of plate and angled away from oral surface. Radials separated by anal series in CD interray. Radianal supports anal X and one other plate, both incorporated into cup. Arms long, uniserial, branching isotomously several times.

Remarks. Bollandocrinus is close in gross morphology to *Poteriocrinites*, but is easily differentiated by the pattern of cup plating. *Bollandocrinus conicus* (Phillips) (Pl. 2, fig. E) is one of three species of this genus that is widely distributed within the British Isles, including Coplow and Salthill quarries (Ausich & Kammer, 2006, appendix A).

Hydreionocrinus de Koninck (Pl. 2, fig. G)
Description. Cup low, bowl-shaped with rounded base. Five low, pentagonal infrabasals apparent laterally. Five basals, five radials and three plates of anal series incorporated in cup (a fourth plate of the anal sac is retained in the figured specimen; Pl. 2, fig. G), the latter supported by two posterior basals (BC and CD). Radial arm facets as wide as radials.

Remarks. The cup of *Hydreionocrinus parkinsoni* Wright (Pl. 2, fig. G) is low and wide, with bilobed excavations in the outer edges of the radial facets that articulate with tongue-like projections on the lowermost arm plate (first primibrachial). This rare species is known from Coplow Quarry; a single specimen from Salthill Quarry is in the private collection of Mr. Vincent Nutall.

Infraclass FLEXIBILIA von Zittel, 1895
Order SAGENOCRINIDA Springer, 1913
Remarks. "Infrabasals abutting on dorsal side of basals, more or less erect, and taking part in the calyx wall. Crown usually small, short, rotund, with arms abutting, frequently interlocking, and closely infolding at the distal ends" (Springer, 1913, p. 203). Dicyclic.

Mespilocrinus de Koninck and Le Hon (Pl. 3, fig. A)
Description. Proximal column circular in section, homeomorphic, not tapered. Crown subglobular. Cup bowl-shaped with three low infrabasals (one small, two large, extending beyond width of column), five basals and five radials. Basals pentagonal to hexagonal; CD basal large, hexagonal, supporting anal X. Anal X higher than wide. Arms short, uniserial, twisted spirally clockwise, strongly incurved distally, branching isotomously and apinnulate, with broad brachial plates. Adjacent arms abutting.

Remarks. The type species, *Mespilocrinus forbesianus* de Koninck & Le Hon (Pl. 3, fig. A), is known from Coplow Quarry (Donovan, 1992, table 1).

Euryocrinus Phillips (Pl. 3, fig. C)
Description. Crown elongate. Cup with flattened base, basals and infrabasals not apparent laterally. Three infrabasals (one small, two large), largely concealed by column, five pentagonal to hexagonal basals and five radials. CD basal elongate, extending into radial circlet and supporting anal series. Arms uniserial, branching isotomously and apinnulate, with broad brachial plates, closely abutting and separated in some parts of crown by columns of a few interbrachial plates.

Remarks. Three species, including *Euryocrinus rofei* Springer (Pl. 3, fig. C) from Coplow Quarry, are known from northern England.

Order TAXOCRINIDA Springer, 1913
Remarks – "Infrabasals usually abutting on dorsal side of basals, but low,

taking little part in the calyx wall. Crown usually elongate, with arms divergent, and not abutting above interbrachial areas. Interbrachials present all round" (Springer 1913, p. 205). Dicyclic.

Taxocrinus Phillips (fig. 6)

Description. Proximal column circular in section, homeomorphic, tapering distally. Crown globular, often elongate. Three infrabasals (one small, two large) largely concealed by column, five basals and five radials. Tubular anal series attached to cup by flexible tegmen. Arms uniserial, strongly incurved distally, branching isotomously and apinnulate, with broad brachial plates. Adjacent arms not in close contact. Primibrachials separated by interprimibrachials.

Remarks. The illustrated specimen of *T. coplowensis* Wright (Fig. 5) shows the base of the crown with the arms splayed out across the bed; this species is only known from Coplow Quarry. Ausich & Kammer (2006, appendix A) noted another two species from the Clitheroe area, including *T. bellmanensis* Wright from Bellman Quarry.

Subclass DISPARIDA Moore & Laudon, 1943

Remarks. Small, monocyclic, gracile, apinnulate crinoids.

Synbathocrinus Phillips (Pl. 3, fig. B)

Description. Cup small, conical to bowl-shaped. Three low basals of unequal size, supporting five larger radials with wide articular facets bearing synarthrial articulations. Anal X slender, elongate and supported in notch on adjacent radials C and D. Tegmen of five oral plates. Although rarely preserved, anal tube elongate and narrow, arms long, slender, unbranched and apinnulate (Pl. 3, fig. B).

Remarks. *Synbathocrinus* is most commonly preserved as small cups. The illustrated specimen of *S. conicus* Phillips (Pl. 3, fig. B) unusually preserves a near-complete crown, although the arms are somewhat disturbed, with the proximal column. *Synbathocrinus conicus* is known from all three quarries at Clitheroe; *S. anglicus* Wright only occurs in Coplow Quarry.

Incerti ordinis

Indeterminate attachment structures **(Pl. 3, fig. D)**
Remarks. Crinoid attachment structures in the Lower Carboniferous are not

as common as might be predicted from the numerous columnals found in the same rocks. This may be due, in part, to attachments being disarticulated and reworked after death. When preserved, attachments are commonly (but not invariably) of the distal radicular runner morphology, adapted for lying recumbent on the sea floor. Radices may either arise from one or all sides (Pl. 3, fig. D) of the modified column. Identification to genus is commonly difficult, at best.

Class BLASTOIDEA Say, 1825

Remarks. The blastoids are an extinct group of echinoderms that died out at the end of the Permian, that is, about 250 million years ago. Blastoids had a consistency of structure not seen in the much more varied, but superficially similar, crinoids. Blastoids had a slender column, a theca composed of three circlets of plates - three basalia, five radials and five deltoids - and multiple, unbranched feeding structures called brachioles. Recognisable blastoids from the Clitheroe area preserve the theca only.

Order FISSICULATA Jaekel, 1918

Remarks. Fissiculates are blastoids with hydrospire slits or spiracular slits that are partly or fully exposed.

Codaster M'Coy (Pl. 4, figs A, B)

Description. Theca cylindrical with a rounded base, rounded pentagonal in oral view, flattened orally, with eight well-exposed hydrospire fields with slits parallel to ambulacra. Three basalia, tall in lateral view, radials taller and overlapping small deltoids. Anal side of theca lacks hydrospire slits.

Remarks. This genus, represented here by *Codaster acutus* M'Coy (Pl. 4, figs A, B), is only known from the Mississippian limestones of England and Ireland. It is locally common in the Grassington area of Yorkshire in association with *Orbitremites* (Joysey, 1955).

Orophocrinus von Seebach (Pl. 4, figs E, F)

Description. Theca conical with a flattened base, pentagonal in oral view, widest just over half the thecal height, with ten elongate spiracular slits bordering ambulacra. Three low basalia, radials tall and deltoids overlap. Between four and eleven hydrospire folds associated with each spiracular slit. Anus separate from spiracular slits.

Remarks. Orophocrinus is locally common in the Mississippian limestones of both North America and western Europe. The illustrated specimen of *Orophocrinus verus* (Cumberland) (Pl. 4, figs E, F) is from Preston in Lancashire. *Orophocrinus* is found at Whitewell, and at both Coplow and Salthill quarries, including *O. verus* and *O. pentagularis* (G.B. Sowerby) (Waters & Sevastopulo, 1985). *Orophocrinus* also occurs in the Upper Devonian of China (J. Savill, written comm. to S.K.D., 2010).

Phaenoschisma Etheridge & Carpenter (Pl. 4, figs C, D)
Description. Theca biconical, widest at about two thirds its height, with narrow base, rounded pentagonal in oral view, with ten elongate spiracular slits bordering ambulacra. Three moderately high basalia, about half the height of tall radials. Deltoids triangular. Hydrospire fields mostly hidden. Number of hydrospire folds reduced adjacent to anus.

Remarks. This genus is known from both North America and Europe. *Phaenoschisma acutum* (G. B. Sowerby) (Pl. 4, figs C, D) is the type species, and is found at Salthill Quarry and Whitewell.

Order GRANATOCRINIDA Bather, 1900
Remarks. Granatocrinids are spiraculate blastoids with a theca that is spherical to elongate globular in shape, ambulacra are narrow and deltoids are exposed in side view. There are either eight spiracles and an anispiracle, nine spiracles and an asymmetrical anispiracle or ten spiracles and a separate anus (Waters & Horowitz, 1993, p. 211).

Mesoblastus Etheridge & Carpenter (Pl. 4, figs G, H)
Description. Theca subglobular, flattened basally, rounded pentagonal in section, with eight spiracles around mouth and a large anispiracle. Three small basalia not apparent laterally. Radials tall, extending almost full height of theca, overlapping deltoids. Small, pentagonal deltoids situated apically. Three long internal hydrospire folds on either side of each ambulacrum.

Remarks. Mesoblastus angulatus (G. B. Sowerby) (Pl. 4, figs G, H) is one of two species of this European genus known from Salthill Quarry, the other being *M. elongatus* (Cumberland). *Mesoblastus* also occurs at Whitewell.

Order PENTREMITIDA Matsumoto, 1929

Remarks. Pentremitids are blastoids with a theca that is spherical to elongate globular in shape, four spiracles and an anispiracle, and deltoids commonly apparent in side view (Waters & Horowitz, 1993, p. 211).

Orbitremites Austin & Austin (Pl. 4, figs I, J)

Description. Theca subglobular, flattened basally, rounded pentagonal in section, with five spiracles around mouth including a large anispiracle. Three small basalia not apparent laterally, radials less than half the height of the theca. Tall, prominent deltoids overlap radials. One long internal hydrospire fold on either side of each ambulacrum.

Remarks. The prominent deltoids differentiate *Orbitremites* from the closely related *Ellipticoblastus* (see below). *Orbitremites* (Pl. 4, figs I, J) may be locally very common, such as within the Mississippian limestones around Grassington, Yorkshire. This genus is also known from Russia (G.D. Sevastopulo, written comm. to S.K.D., May 2010) and the Permian of West Timor, Indonesia (J. Savill written comm. to S.K.D., 2010).

Ellipticoblastus Fay (Pl. 4, figs K, L)

Description. Theca high subglobular, flattened basally, rounded pentagonal in section, with five spiracles around the mouth including large anispiracle. Three small basalia not apparent laterally, radials more than half the height of the theca, overlapping smaller deltoids. One internal hydrospire fold on either side of each ambulacrum.

Remarks. The high radials of *Ellipticoblastus* distinguish it from closely similar *Orbitremites*. *Ellipticoblastus* and *Orbitremites* are known from England and Ireland. *Ellipticoblastus ellipticus* (G. B. Sowerby) (Pl. 4, figs K, L) occurs at both Salthill and Bellman quarries, and at Whitewell.

Class ECHINOIDEA Leske, 1778

Remarks. Echinoids or sea urchins will be familiar to any beachcomber. Most Palaeozoic members of this class differ from extant echinoids by commonly having multiple plate columns in the ambulacra and interambulacra; post-Palaeozoic echinoids invariably have two columns of plate in every ambulacrum and every interambulacrum. Mississippian echinoid tests are typically preserved in a collapsed, flattened and commonly dissociated condition.

Family PALAECHINIDAE M'Coy, 1844

Remarks. Palaeozoic echinoids with plates weakly imbricated, enlarged adradial ambulacral plates, interambulacra of more than two columns of plates, imperforate tubercles and no perignathic girdle (Kier, 1966, p. U309).

Melonechinus Meek & Worthen (Pl. 5, figs A, B)

Description. Test spherical, composed of thick, tessellated polygonal plates. Apical disc small with five genital plates, each perforated by multiple gonopores, and five ocular plates. Ambulacra with 6-12 columns of small polygonal plates each with a simple pore-pair; plates of the two central columns are widest, with bands of small demiplates developed adradially; no internal flanges. Interambulacra composed of 4-11 columns of subpolygonal plates slightly larger than ambulacral plates. Miliary granules scattered, plates appear smooth. Peristome small. Lantern simple; no internal perignathic girdle.

Remarks. The illustrated *Melonechinus etheridgei* (Keeping) shows a common pattern of preservation; the surface in contact with the seafloor after collapse preserves plate columns, whereas the upper surface was partly disarticulated prior to burial (Pl. 5, figs A, B respectively). This species is known from both Bellman and Coplow quarries.

Family ARCHAEOCIDARIDAE M'Coy, 1844

Remarks. Test flexible due to imbricate plating, interambulacral plates in four or more columns, primary tubercles perforate and noncrenulate, and ambulacral pores uniserial (Fell, 1966, p. U317).

Lepidocidaris Meek & Worthen (Pl. 6, fig. B)

Description. Test subspherical, perhaps flattened orally and apically, flexible. Ambulacra formed of two columns of plates tending towards triads, with every third plate larger, though not fused into compound plates; pores uniserial. Interambulacra formed of six to eight columns of plates which imbricate aborally and laterally from the centre, and over ambulacra at adradius. Primary tubercles large, perforate, non-crenulate, surrounded by raised swollen scrobicular circles. Spines cylindrical, longitudinally striate.

Remarks. The large and distinctive primary tubercles of *Lepidocidaris squamosa anglica* Hawkins (Pl. 6, fig. B) contrast to those of other echinoids illustrated herein. Archaeocidarid spines and interambulacral plates are known from Salthill and Bellman quarries.

Family PROTEROCIDARIDAE Smith, 1984

Remarks. Flattened test with imbricate plating, ambulacra composed of two or more columns of plates with small and simple pore-pairs adapically and large pore-pairs with circular rims adorally, interambulacra composed of multiple columns of thin rhomboidal plates with small tubercles (Smith, 1984, p. 147).

Perischodomus M'Coy (Pl. 6, fig. A)

Description. Test spherical. Apical disc relatively small; genital plates low, wide with five to seven pores; separated by oculars. Ambulacra narrow, with two columns of plates with some at the ambitus not in contact with interambulacral plates; plates larger adorally; pores biserial at ambitus. Interambulacra wide with at least five columns of plates; plates imbricate aborally and laterally from the centre, and over ambulacra at adradius; primary tubercles perforate, eccentric, present on adradial plates with scrobicule and secondary tubercles; central plates may or may not have primary tubercles, may have secondary tubercles. Spines tapering.

Remarks. The illustrated, disarticulated test of *Perischodomus biserialis* M'Coy (Pl. 6, fig. A) preserves evidence of imbrication along the upper left quadrant. Plates of *Perischodomus* have a relatively sparse distribution of secondary tubercles of the surface, unlike the evenly distributed granules of *Melonechinus*. Known from Coplow Quarry.

Glossary

Crinoids (adapted from Donovan et al., 2008)

abaxial — away from the axis; eccentric.

anal pyramid — a low, conical structure on the tegmen around the anus.

anal sac — a multiplated, elongate, commonly ornate, bag-like structure in cladids, flexibles and disparids that elevates the opening of the anus (at or near the end of the sac) above the oral surface. Anal sacs may be shorter than, as long as or longer than the arms.

anal series — the plates between the anus and the most proximal plate of the posterior interray.

anal tube — a tube in camerates that elevates the opening of the anus above the oral surface.

anal X — found in disparid, cladid and flexible crinoids. A plate located in the CD interray, the lowest of the anal series, situated within or above the radial circlet.

apinnulate — arm lacks pinnules.

arm facet — articular facet on a radial plate on which the arm articulates.

arms — serial, elongate, upright and commonly branched structures, elevated above the oral surface of the calyx and adapted for capturing plankton for food using the tube feet.

attachment structure — the method whereby the crinoid attaches to a substrate, commonly a root-like structure near or at the end of the column, or a multiplated structure at the base of the column.

axial canal — the canal that follows the long axis of the column and, in life, includes certain soft tissues, particularly nervous tissues. Commonly central and apparent as an opening on each articular facet of a columnal. Commonly circular or pentagonal in outline. The opening of the axial canal on an articular facet is termed the lumen.

basal concavity — depression in the basal circlet of a monocyclic crinoid. The proxistele attaches to the articular facet in the centre of the depression.

basals — the crinoid cup is composed of two or three (rarely four) circlets of plates, exclusive of the tegmen. Each circlet is commonly formed of five plates, although these show considerable variation between genera. In a dicyclic cup, the lowest plate circlet, the infrabasals, support the basals, which support the radials. In a monocyclic cup the basals are the lower circlet. Basals are offset from infrabasals and radials.

BC interray — see rays.

brachials — ossicles of the arms, generally with a U-shaped section, the groove being adoral in position.

C, C ray — see rays.

calyx — the part of the crown below the free arms, formed from the cup, fixed arms, interradials and (if present) interbrachials, but not the tegmen (compare with theca).

CD interray — see rays.

column – the part of the stem between the attachment structure and cup. In most crinoids the column elevates the crown above the sea floor.

crown — the part of the crinoid above the stem, consisting of the calyx and free arms.

cup — lowest part of the calyx/crown, consisting of two (monocyclic) or three circlets of plates (dicyclic). The arms form a continuous series of plates articulating with the topmost plates of the cup (radials).

D, D ray — see rays.

dicyclic — a cup comprised of two basal circlets, the lower infrabasals supporting the basals. The basals, in turn, support the radial circlet.

fixed arms — proximal, inflexible series of brachials at base of arms that are rigidly sutured into the calyx. Most typical of camerates, but also found in other groups.

free arms — the flexible parts of the arms above the calyx.

homeomorphic — a column or part of a column composed of identical columnals.

infrabasals — the lowest plate circlet in a dicyclic crinoid cup.

interbrachials — plates that occur between branches of an arm.

interray — see rays.

isotomously — equal branching of arms.

junior synonym — a second name erroneously given to a fossil species. The first-given name (=senior synonym) takes precedence.

meric sutures — straight or zigzag suture apparent on the latera of pentameric columns.

monocyclic — a cup comprised of one basal circlet supporting the radial circlet (that is, an infrabasal circlet is absent).

oral plates — five articulated, tegminal plates in interradial positions and protecting the mouth.

pentameric — columns in which each columnal is formed from a circlet of (most commonly) five wedge-shaped ossicles (pentameres) of equal size.

pinnulate — possessing pinnules, that is, the slender, unbranched, minor branches arising from the arms in certain crinoid groups.

plates — calcareous ossicles of the echinoderm endoskeleton.

platycrinitids — members of the crinoid family Platycrinitidae Austin & Austin, including *Platycrinites*, *Pleurocrinus* and *Brahmacrinus*.

primanal — the lowermost plate of the anal series in camerate crinoids.

primibrachials — the most proximal series of arm plates, supported by the radials. The highest primibrachial in branched arms is the primaxillary; in unbranched arms, all brachials are primibrachials.

radials — the highest circlet of plates of the cup, supported by the basals and supporting the arms.

radianal — an inferradial in the C ray that supports the anal X plate of the anal opening.

radicular — bearing root-like extensions, branched or unbranched, either as the distal termination of the column or arising from one side of the dististele. Radicles/radices may be unbranched or branched.

rays — the five rays of a crinoid, each including a radial plate of the cup that supports an arm, are named A, B, C, D and E. These are separated by interrays AB, BC, CD, DE and EA. The CD interray is identified as the position of the anal series and is regarded as posterior. On the opposite side of the cup is the A ray (anterior).

secundibrachials — the two arm branches supported by the primaxillary. The highest secundibrachial in arms that branch more than twice is the secundaxillary.

tegmen — the adoral part of the theca, situated above the free arms. The tegmen may be calcified and multiplated, particularly in camerates, and bears the anal opening and associated structures (such as an anal tube or sac).

theca — the 'box-like' part of a crinoid, that region above the column and below the free arms, composed of the calyx and tegmen.

type series — The group of specimens upon which a species is originally defined.

uniserial — plates arranged in a line, one after another. For example, the arms of many species of crinoids are typically uniserial, at least in part.

Blastoids (adapted from Donovan et al., 2003)

ambulacrum — one of five food gathering areas radiating aborally from mouth. Brachioles are supported along either side of an ambulacrum, flanking a central main food groove. Ambulacra are radial in position and named A to E. The A ray/ambulacrum is anterior and is situated on the opposite side of the test to the anus in the CD interray. The ambulacra are separated by the higher plate circlets of the theca, that is, radials and deltoids.

anispiracle — enlarged opening in summit portion of posterior interray of a spiraculate blastoid, formed by the union of the anal opening and the posterior spiracle or spiracles.

basalia — basal circlet of plates in blastoid theca, normally consisting of two large (zygous) and one small (azygous) plates.

brachiole — simple, unbranched, biserial appendages of the theca, attached at the edges of ambulacra.

deltoids — the blastoid theca consists of three circlets of plates, three basalia, five radials and five deltoids. The deltoids are a circlet of plates near the summit of the theca and supported by the radials, and situated in the angles made by adjacent ambulacra.

hydrospire — folds of the radial and deltoid plates into the theca, with thin walls, and situated parallel to and adjacent to either side of an ambulacrum. Where exposed, the folds have the appearance of parallel slits on the surface of the theca.

radials — five cleft plates above basalia, radial in position, each receiving the aboral extremity of an ambulacrum.

spiracle — five commonly rounded openings within deltoid plates surrounding the mouth and interradial in position (see ambulacrum, above), that is, supported by the deltoid plates. In some taxa a septum within the ambulacrum is exposed, dividing the spiracle into two.

spiracular slit — an elongate spiracle flanking an ambulacrum.

spiraculate — a blastoid with spiracles. In some taxa the posterior spiracle is enlarged as the anispiracle.

theca — the 'box-like' part of a blastoid, that region above the column and below the brachioles.

Echinoids (adapted from Lewis et al., 2007)

adapically — towards the apex of the test, that is, the apical disc.

adorally — towards the oral surface of the text, that is, the peristome.

adradial — towards a radial suture, that is, the mid-line of an ambulacrum.

ambitus — the widest part of the circumference of the test.

ambulacra — five rays of the test, radial in position, formed of pored plates which support the radial water vessel and associated tube feet (singular, ambulacrum).

apical disc — a group of plates at the apex of the test, divided into five ocular plates at the top of each ambulacral zone, and up to five genital plates, interradial in position, and through which the gonads open via genital pores. The sieve-like madreporite is present on one of the genital plates. The disc may also include additional plates.

biserial — two columns of plates or two apparent columns of pores.

column — a series of plates in a vertical sequence.

demiplate — an ambulacral plate that is in contact with the adradial suture, but not the perradial suture.

genital plate — plate of the apical disc which has one or more pores for the discharge of genital products.

gonopores — openings in the genital plates through which eggs and sperm are released.

imbricate plating — overlapping plates that are able to move over one another.

imperforate (tubercle) — a tubercle that is not pierced by a hole.

interambulacra — five areas of the test that lie between the five ambulacra.

lantern — the jaw mechanism of an echinoid made of about 40 components.

madreporite — part of one of the genital plates which has numerous perforations for ingress of water and for pressure equalisation.

miliary granules — minute tubercles that bore equally small spines.

ocular plate — one of the five radial plates of the apical disc.

perforate — the hole in a tubercle and a radiole. The hole has a supporting rod inserted into it in life.

perignathic girdle — the attachment structure for the muscles of the lantern. This may be continuous or discontinuous.

peristome — the aperture in the test which surrounds the mouth, and which is covered in life by a membrane.

pore pairs — the holes in ambulacral plates through which pass the tube feet. One pair of pores is associated with one tube foot.

primary tubercle — the main tubercle of an ambulacral or interambulacral plate which articulates with a primary radiole.

scrobicule — the depressed ring that surrounds a tubercle and which serves for the attachment of muscles operating the spine. A scrobicular circlet is a ring of tubercles which surround the large, primary interambualcral tubercles in archaeocidarids and bear flattened secondary spines. These protected the soft tissues at the base of the primary spine.

secondary tubercles — tubercles that surround a primary tubercle or which are situated elsewhere on the test.

spines — erect, slender, cylindrical structures arising from test plates, of various sizes and fulfilling different functions.

tesselated — plates of the test forming a rigid mosaic-like structure.

test — the 'shell' of an echinoid.

triads — a group of three, for example, a repeating pattern of test plates in groups of three.

tubercles — large or small domed spine bases of the text.

uniserial — a single column of plates or pore pairs.

Acknowledgements
Fig.1 James Wright (1878-1957) is after http://freepages.genealogy. rootsweb.ancestry.com/~barnettwright/peter_wright.htm. Fig. 2 Stanley Westhead (1910-1986) is after Clitheroe Advertiser and Times, article dated 17th July 1986. The many excellent images that appear in the plates and Figures 3-6 were kindly taken by Phil Crabb (Photographic Unit, The Natural History Museum, London). We thank Jeremy J. Savill, and Professors Thomas W. Kammer (West Virginia University, Morgantown), George D. Sevastopulo (Trinity College, Dublin) and Johnny A. Waters (Appalachian State University, Boone, North Carolina) for their insightful reviews of an earlier version of this chapter.

References
Anon (1983): Salthill Quarry SSSI, Clitheroe, Lancashire: 'geology goes to town'. *Earth Science Conservation, No. **20**, pp. 11-14.*

Ausich, W. I. & Kammer, T. W. (2006): Stratigraphical and geographical distributions of Mississippian (Lower Carboniferous) Crinoidea from England and Wales. *Proceedings of the Yorkshire Geological Society, Vol. **56**, pp. 91-109.*

Ausich, W. I. & Kammer, T. W. (2009): Generic concepts in the Platycrinitidae Austin and Austin, 1842 (Class Crinoidea). *Journal of Paleontology, Vol. **83**, pp. 694-717.*

Ausich, W. I. & Sevastopulo, G. D. (2001): The Lower Carboniferous (Tournasian) crinoids from Hook Head, County Wexford, Ireland. *Monograph of the Palaeontographical Society, Vol. 155 (no. 617), 137 pp.*

Bather, F. A. (1900): The Blastoidea. In Lankester, E. R. (ed.). *A Treatise on Zoology. Part III. Echinodermata, pp. 28-93.* A. & C. Black, London.

Beaver, H. H., Fay, R. O., Macurda, D. B., Jr., Moore, R. C. & Wanner, J. (1967): Blastoids. In Moore, R. C. (ed.). *Treatise on Invertebrate Paleontology, Part S, Echinodermata 1(2), pp. S297-S455.* Geological Society of America, Boulder, and University of Kansas Press, Lawrence.

Bowden, A., Webster, M. & Mitcham, T. (1997): Salthill Quarry geology trail. *Geologists' Association Guide, Vol. 58, 30 pp.*

Clarkson, E. N. K. (1998): *Invertebrate Palaeontology and Evolution.* 4th edition. Blackwell Science, Oxford, xvi+452 pp.

Donovan, S. K. (1988): Obituary notice: Stanley Westhead. *Proceedings of the Geologists' Association, Vol. 99, p. 152.*

Donovan, S. K. (1992): A field guide to the fossil echinoderms of Coplow, Bellman and Salthill Quarries, Clitheroe, Lancashire. *North West Geologist, Vol. 2, pp. 33-54.*

Donovan, S. K., Lewis, D. N. & Crabb, P. (2003): Lower Carboniferous echinoderms of northwest England. *Palaeontological Association Fold-Out Fossils, Vol. 1, 12 pp.*

Donovan, S. K., Lewis, D. N., Crabb, P. & Widdison, R. E. (2008): A field guide to the Silurian Echinodermata of the British Isles: Part 2 – Crinoidea, minor groups and discussion. *Proceedings of the Yorkshire Geological Society, Vol. 57, pp. 29-60.*

Donovan, S. K. & Veltkamp, C. J. (1990): *Barycrinus* (Crinoidea) from the Lower Carboniferous of England. *Journal of Paleontology, Vol. 64, pp. 988-992.*

Donovan, S. K. & Westhead, S. (1987): *Platycrinites contractus* (Gilbertson) and a new *Platycrinites* from the Lower Carboniferous of northern England. *Proceedings of the Geologists' Association, Vol.* **98**, *pp. 211-215.*

Fell, H. B. (1966): Cidaroids. In Moore, R. C. (ed.). *Treatise on Invertebrate Paleontology. Part U, Echinodermata 3(1), pp. U312-U339.* Geological Society of America, New York, and University of Kansas Press, Lawrence.

Grayson, R. (1981): Salthill Quarry Geological Trail. *Nature Conservancy Council, London, 26 pp.*

Jaekel, O. (1918): Phylogenie und System der Pelmatozoen. *Paläontologische Zeitschrift, Vol.* **3**, *pp. 1-128.*

Joysey, K. A. (1955): On the geological distribution of Carboniferous blastoids in the Craven area, based on a study of their occurrence in the Yoredale series of Grassington, Yorkshire. *Quarterly Journal of the Geological Society, London, Vol.* **111**, *pp. 209-224.*

Kammer, T. W. & Ausich, W. I. (2006): The "Age of Crinoids": a Mississippian biodiversity spike coincident with widespread carbonate ramps. *Palaios, Vol.* **21**, *pp. 238-248.*

Kier, P. M. (1966): Noncidaroid Paleozoic echinoids. In Moore, R. C. (ed.). *Treatise on Invertebrate Paleontology. Part U, Echinodermata 3(1), pp. U298-U312.* Geological Society of America, New York, and University of Kansas Press, Lawrence.

Lewis, D. N., Donovan, S. K., Crabb, P. & Gladwell, D. J. (2007): A field guide to the Silurian Echinodermata of the British Isles: Part 1 – Eleutherozoa and Rhombifera. *Scripta Geologica, Vol.* **134**, *27-59.*

Leske, N. G. (1778): *Iacobi Theodori Klein Naturalis disposito Echinodermatum, Edita et aucta a N. G. Leske.* Lipsiae, xx+278 pp.

Matsumoto, H. (1929): Outline of a classification of Echinodermata. *Science Reports of the Tohoku University, Vol.* **13**, *pp. 27-33.* [Not seen.]

M'Coy, F. (1844): *Carboniferous Limestone Fossils of Ireland.* Dublin, pp. 5-207. [Not seen.]

Melville, R. V. (1958): Obituary notice: James Wright. *Proceedings of the Geologists' Association, Vol.* **69**, 71-72.

Melville, R. V. & Durham, J. W. (1966): Skeletal morphology. In Moore, R. C. (ed.), *Treatise on Invertebrate Paleontology, Part U, Echinodermata 3(1), pp. U220-U251.* Geological Society of America, New York, and University of Kansas Press, Lawrence.

Miller, J. & Grayson, R. F. (1972): Origin and structure of the Lower Viséan "reef" limestones near Clitheroe, Lancashire. *Proceedings of the Yorkshire Geological Society, Vol.* **38**, *pp. 607-638.*

Miller, J. S. (1821): *A Natural History of the Crinoidea or Lily-Shaped Animals, with observation on the genera Asteria, Euryale, Comatula and Marsupites.* C. Frost, Bristol, 150 pp.

Moore, R. C. (1978): Dedication. In Moore, R. C. & Teichert, C. (eds). *Treatise on Invertebrate Paleontology. Part T, Echinodermata 2(1), pp. T2-T7.* Geological Society of America, Boulder, and University of Kansas Press, Lawrence.

Moore, R. C., Lane, N. G. & Strimple, H. L. (1978): Order Cladida Moore & Laudon, 1943. In Moore, R. C. & Teichert, C. (eds). *Treatise on Invertebrate Paleontology, Part T, Echinodermata 2(2), pp. T578-T759.* Geological Society of America, Boulder, and University of Kansas Press, Lawrence.

Moore, R. C. & Laudon, L. R. (1943): Evolution and classification of Paleozoic crinoids. *Geological Society of America, Special Paper, Vol.* **46**, *pp. 1-153.*

Moore, R. C. & Teichert, C. (eds) (1978): *Treatise on Invertebrate Paleontology. Part T. Echinodermata 2.* In three volumes. Geological Society of America, Boulder, and University of Kansas Press, Lawrence, xxxviii+1027 pp.

Say, T. (1825): On two genera and several species of Crinoidea. *Academy of Natural Sciences of Philadelphia, Journal (series 1), Vol.* **4**, *pp. 289-296.* [Not seen.]

Smith, A. B. (1984): *Echinoid Palaeobiology.* Allen & Unwin, London, xii+190 pp.

Springer, F. (1913): Crinoidea. In Zittel, K. A. von (Eastman, C. R., ed.). *Text-Book of Paleontology, pp. 173-245.* MacMillan & Co., London.

Wachsmuth, C. & Springer, F. (1885): Revision of the Palaeocrinoidea, part III, section 1. Discussion of the classification and relations of the brachiate crinoids, and conclusion of the generic descriptions. *Proceedings of the Academy of Natural Sciences of Philadelphia, pp. 223-264.*

Waters, J. A. & Horowitz, A. S. (1983): Ordinal-level evolution in the Blastoidea. *Lethaia, Vol. 26, pp. 207-213.*

Waters, J. A. & Sevastopulo, G. D. (1985): The paleobiogeography of Irish and British Lower Carboniferous blastoids. In Keegan, B.F. & O'Connor, B.D.S. (eds). *Echinodermata. Proceedings of the Fifth International Echinoderm Conference, Galway, 24-29 September, 1984, pp. 141-147.* Balkema, Rotterdam.

Webster, G. D., Waters, J. & Xiuqin Chen (2009): Revision of the Chen and Yao Devonian to Permian crinoids from western Yunnan. *Palaeobiodiversity and Palaeoenvironments, Vol. 89, pp. 119-160.*

Westhead, S. (1979): Carboniferous crinoids from the Clitheroe area. *Proceedings of the North-East Lancashire Group of the Geologists' Association, Vol. 2, pp. 465-496.*

Wright, J. (1950-1960): A monograph of the British Carboniferous Crinoidea. *Monograph of the Palaeontographical Society, Vol. 1, pt. 1, pp. i-xxx+ 1-24 [1950]; pt. 2, pp. 25-46 [1951]; pt. 3, pp. 47-102 [1951]; pt. 4, pp. 103- 148 [1952]; pt. 5, pp. 149-190 [1954]: Vol. 2, pt. 1, pp. 191-254 [1955]; pt. 2, pp. 255-272 [1955]; pt. 3, pp. 273-306 [1956]; pt. 4, pp. 307-328 [1958]; pt. 5, pp. 329-347 [1960].*

Zittel, K. A. von (1895): *Grundzüge der Palaeontologie (Palaeozoologie), 1st edition. R. Oldenbourg, München.* 971 pp.

FIGURES

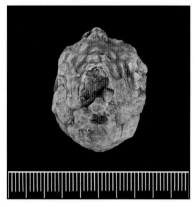

Fig. 3   *Thinocrinus westheadi* (Wright)
(after Donovan et al., 2003, pl. 2, fig. 1), BMNH E71176,
lateral view. Scale bar in mm.

Fig. 4   *Platycrinites jameswrighti* Donovan & Westhead
(compare with Donovan & Westhead, 1987, fig. 2A),
lateral view. Scale bar in mm.

Fig. 5 *Poteriocrinites crassus* J. S. Miller
(after Donovan et al., 2003, pl. 3, fig. 4), BMNH E71393,
lateral view of cup. Scale bar in mm.

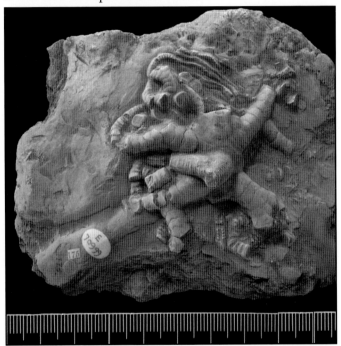

Fig. 6 *Taxocrinus coplowensis* Wright
(after Donovan et al., 2003, pl. 4, fig. 3), BMNH E70999,
base of crown with arms splayed out, proximal column to left.
Scale bar in mm.

PLATE 1

Lateral views of crinoid thecae.

Fig. A. *Gilbertsocrinus mammillaris* Phillips
(after Donovan et al., 2003, pl. 1, fig. 1b), BMNH 46265.

Fig. B. *Amphoracrinus turgidus* Wright
(after Donovan et al., 2003, pl. 1, fig. 2b), BMNH E71261.

Fig. C. *Eumorphocrinus excelsus* Wright
(after Donovan et al., 2003, pl. 2, fig. 3), BMNH E71187.

Fig. D. *Pimlicocrinus brevicalix* (Rofe)
(after Donovan et al., 2003, pl. 1, fig. 6b), BMNH E71229.

Fig. E. *Actinocrinites anglicus* (Wright)
(after Donovan et al., 2003, pl. 2, fig. 2b), BMNH E71208.

Fig. F. *Amphoracrinus gilbertsoni* J. S. Miller
(after Donovan et al., 2003, pl. 1, fig. 5b), BMNH E71175.

Fig. G. *Mcoycrinus globosus* (Phillips)
(after Donovan et al., 2003, pl. 1, fig. 3b), BMNH E70903.

Fig. H. *Pleurocrinus megastylus* (M'Coy)
(after Donovan et al., 2003, pl. 2, fig. 6b), BMNH E71356.

Fig. I. *Actinocrinites coplowensis* Wright
(after Donovan et al., 2003, pl. 1, fig. 7b), BMNH E71060.

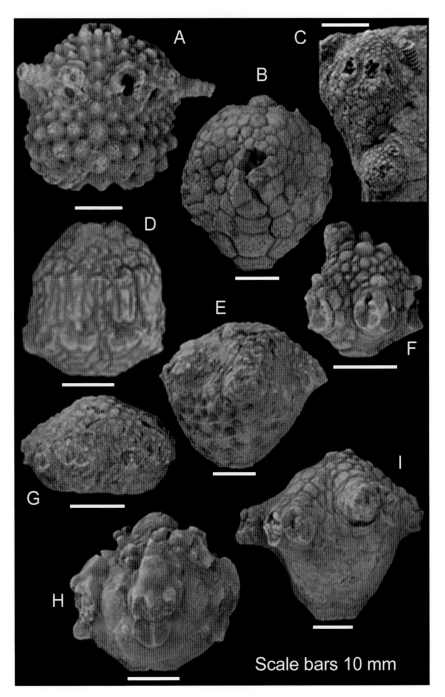

Scale bars 10 mm

PLATE 2

Lateral views of crinoid thecae except B and C.

Fig. A. *Brahmacrinus ponderosus* Sollas
(after Donovan et al., 2003, pl. 2, fig. 7b), BMNH 40323.

Figs B, C. *Platycrinites* sp.
(after Donovan et al., 2003, pl. 2, fig. 4b, a, respectively), BMNH
40334. (B) Pluricolumnal in lateral view. (C) Articular facet.

Fig. D. *Cyathocrinites planus* J. S. Miller
(after Donovan et al., 2003, pl. 3, fig. 7b), BMNH E71151.

Fig. E. *Bollandocrinus conicus* (Phillips)
(after Donovan et al., 2003, pl. 4, fig. 6a), BMNH E71143.

Fig. F. *Pleurocrinus coronatus* Goldfuss
(after Donovan et al., 2003, pl. 2, fig. 5b), BMNH E71381.

Fig. G. *Hydreionocrinus parkinsoni* Wright
(after Donovan et al., 2003, pl. 4, fig. 2b), BMNH E70825.

Fig. H. *Barycrinus ribblesdalensis* (Wright)
(after Donovan et al., 2003, pl. 3, fig. 5b), BMNH E26425.

Scale bars 10 mm

PLATE 3

Crinoids from Clitheroe.

Fig. A. *Mespilocrinus forbesianus* de Koninck & Le Hon
(after Donovan et al., 2003, pl. 4, fig. 4), BMNH E71026,
proximal column, cup and disarticulated arms.

Fig. B. *Synbathocrinus conicus* Phillips
(after Donovan et al., 2003, pl. 3, fig. 1), BMNH E70997,
proximal column and crown.

Fig. C. *Euryocrinus rofei* Springer
(after Donovan et al., 2003, pl. 4, fig. 8), BMNH E70998, arms.

Fig. D. Indeterminate crinoid attachment structure
(after Donovan et al., 2003, pl. 4, fig. 7), BMNH E25026.

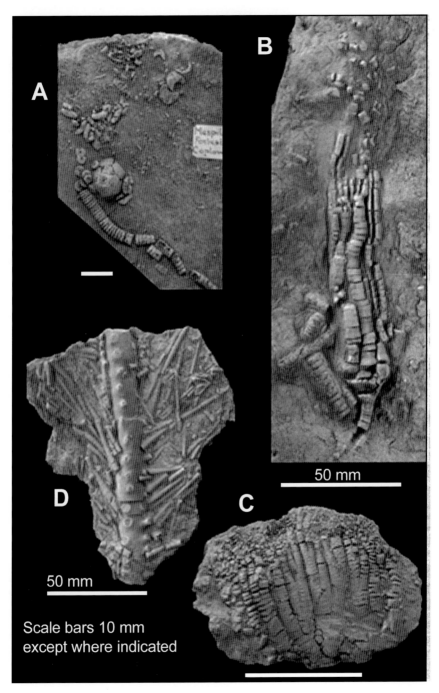

Scale bars 10 mm
except where indicated

PLATE 4

Blastoids from northwest England.

Figs A, B.   *Codaster acutus* M'Coy
(after Donovan et al., 2003, pl. 5, fig. 1a, b), BMNH 75908,
(A) oral and (B) lateral views.

Figs C, D.   *Phaenoschisma acutum* (G. B. Sowerby)
(after Donovan et al., 2003, pl. 5, fig. 6a, b), BMNH E8130,
(C) oral and (D) lateral views.

Figs E, F.   *Orophocrinus verus* (Cumberland)
(after Donovan et al., 2003, pl. 5, fig. 2a, b), BMNH E847,
(E) oral and (F) lateral views.

Figs G, H.   *Mesoblastus angulatus* (G. B. Sowerby)
(after Donovan et al., 2003, pl. 5, fig. 3a, b), BMNH E780,
(G) oral and (H) lateral views.

Figs I, J.   *Orbitremites derbiensis* (G. B. Sowerby)
(after Donovan et al., 2003, pl. 5, fig. 4a, b), BMNH E30497,
(I) oral and (J) lateral views.

Figs K, L.   *Elliptocoblastus ellipticus* (G. B. Sowerby)
(after Donovan et al., 2003, pl. 5, fig. 5a, b), BMNH E8070,
(K) oral and (L) lateral views.

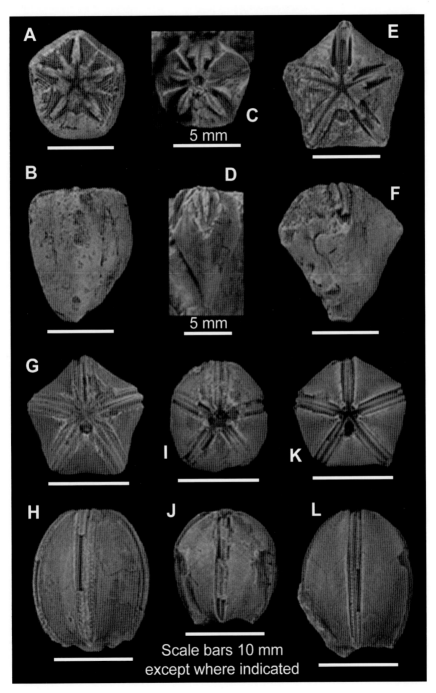

5 mm

5 mm

Scale bars 10 mm
except where indicated

PLATE 5

Figs A, B. The Mississippian echinoid *Melonechinus etheridgi* (Keeping) (after Donovan et al., 2003, pl. 5, fig. 7a, b), BMNH E82729, both sides of a collapsed test. (A) shows the 'lower' surface that was preserved in contact with the underlying sediment surface with plates still well-organised in columns; interambulacra consist of multiple columns of large plates, ambulacra include multiple columns of small plates. (B) shows the 'upper' surface in which plates partially disarticulated before final burial.

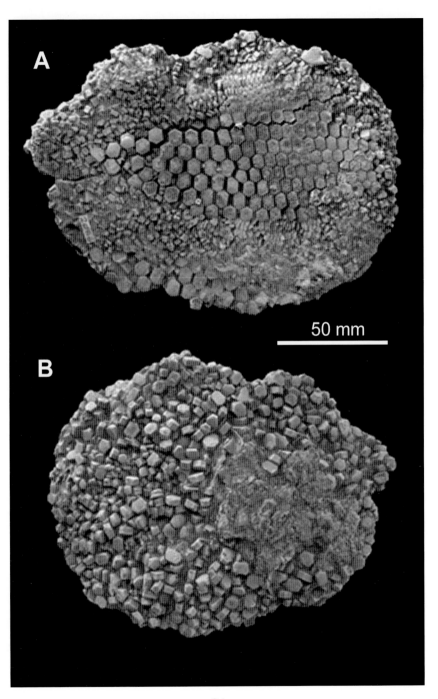

PLATE 6

Mississippian echinoids.

Fig. A. *Perischodomus biserialis* M'Coy
(after Donovan et al., 2003, pl. 5, fig. 9), BMNH E82727,
collapsed test.

Fig. B. *Lepidocidaris squamosa anglica* Hawkins
(after Donovan et al., 2003, pl. 5, fig. 8), BMNH E75240,
collapsed test preserving spines. Note large primary tubercles, in
contrast to other echinoids from Clitheroe.

Chapter 4

Pendle Hill – a turbulent past

Ian Kane

Statoil ASA Research Centre, Bergen, Norway.

Pendle Hill (557 m) is located in the north-east of Lancashire, approximately 5 km south-west of Clitheroe and lies within the Forest of Bowland Area of Outstanding Natural Beauty. The hill is one of the most striking geomorphologic features of the landscape in the Craven and Pendle area. Aside from the geological importance of Pendle Hill, there are a wealth of historically important events associated with it. The very name Pendle Hill has a long and varied history, stemming from the old Cumbric pen and the Old English hyll which together gave the thirteenth century name of Pennul or Penhul, both meaning 'hill'. As with many old place names, the meaning became lost in the mists of time so it seemed only sensible to tag 'Hill' onto the end, to give 'Pendle Hill', or perhaps more correctly, 'Hillhill Hill'!

The dramatic steep-sided flanks of Pendle Hill result from the sharp contrast between the mudstone-rich rocks at the base of the flanks and the hard sandstones of the Pendle Grit which appear towards the top of the hill. The mudstones are much more susceptible to weathering and erosion than the well-cemented sandstones; for this reason many of the hills and escarpments in the district have a similar character, e.g., Longridge Fell and Waddington Fell. It is from here that the Pendle Grit takes its name, originally being referred to as the Pendle Top Grit.

The Pendle Grit (and associated sedimentary rocks which together comprise the Pendle Grit Formation) is the oldest of the major Millstone Grit sandstones, and is the focus of this chapter. The Pendle Grit is quite different to most of the Millstone Grit sandstones; its occurrence and character at Pendle Hill is discussed and placed into the larger scale context of the Pendle Grit depositional system within the Craven Basin.

The Craven Basin and Bowland Sub-Basin

A sedimentary basin is a depression of the Earth's crust formed through some mixture of tectonic forces, subsidence, and erosional processes. As basins are topographic low points, they can act as sites of sediment accumulation, through terrestrial and marine sediment transport and depositional processes. The Craven Basin consists of a series of linked sub-basins and 'highs' (high points within the basin) (**fig. 1**). The basin formed between tectonically stable high points known as blocks; it is bounded to the northwest by the Lake District High, to the northeast by the Askrigg Block, and by the Central Lancashire High to the south. The Craven Basin may be divided into two principal sub-basins, the Lancaster Fells Sub-Basin to the north, and the Bowland Sub-Basin to the south. The two basins are partly separated by a high point know as the Bowland High.

The Craven Basin forms part of a larger system of basins that developed during the late Devonian to Early Carboniferous periods. These formed due to a regime of extensional tectonics – movement of the Earth's plates acting to pull apart the crust. This extension was directed from the north and south, with the result that the crust was thinned across much of England, Wales and Scotland. As the crust was pulled apart it resulted in deformation, forming a series of faults, formed by brittle deformation of the crust, i.e., earthquakes, which separated areas that were relatively stable from areas which were subsiding downwards. The high points became the 'blocks' and the low points became the 'basins'. Some of these faults are still sites of earthquake activity, for example, the Skipton Earthquake of 1944 which was focused on the Craven Fault Zone; this fault zone separates the more stable Askrigg Block in the north from the Craven Basin in the south. The earthquake resulted in damage to surface drains and a bridge, and produced an audible 'rumble'. The major basin margin faults in this area occur within the Craven Fault Zone, and are known as the North, Mid and South Craven faults. The Craven faults juxtapose the green uplands that are typical of the limestone areas to the north from the darker lowland areas of the south.

The early part of the sedimentary history of the Craven Basin consists of deposition of thick limestone sequences (see Chapter 2). In total, the basin was filled with over 4 km of limestones and mudstones. This seems like an extraordinary thickness of sediment, but the basin was never actually this deep. The weight of sediment in the basin, weighing down on the Earth's crust which had already been thinned by tectonic stretching, allowed the basin to subside, and continuously generate space into which more sediment could be deposited. Consequently the limestone sequence on the blocks is much thinner than in the basins.

The shallow seas of the Early Carboniferous, in which corals and other carbonate producing organisms thrived, gradually gave way to deeper seas as the basin subsided at a rate greater than carbonates (limestones) were produced. Eventually, limestone deposition was restricted to the high points separating the basins, for example the Askrigg Block, or the Derbyshire Platform to the south. The subsiding basins deepened and became anoxic. Sediment deposition now became dominated by settling of mud and fine grained material that had been floating in suspension. This 'hemipelagic' deposition occurred at an incredibly slow rate. Nevertheless, a thick sequence of mud built up, occasionally interspersed with limestones which collapsed from high points and flowed as turbidity currents along the seafloor to low points within the basin (for example the Pendleside Limestone exposed on the flanks of Pendle Hill). Meanwhile, to the north, a major river and delta system transporting sand and mud was advancing southwards.

The Millstone Grit Group

The first significant clue that the coarse-grained sediments of the Millstone Grit were advancing towards the basin is the deposition of the Pendleside Sandstone, a thin sandstone-shale sequence now best exposed on the lower flanks of Pendle Hill. To the north, for example, at Rams Clough in the Trough of Bowland, the Pendleside Sandstone is represented by a single 20 cm thick bed. This unit was deposited on the sea floor by episodic turbidity currents flowing into the basin from the north. Overall, deposition at this time was still dominated by hemipelagic fallout of mud, so the Pendleside Sandstone is effectively encased within the thick sequence of mudstones known as the Lower Bowland Shales. A further thick sequence of mudstone follows (the Upper Bowland Shales), punctuated by the deposition of another minor sandstone, the Hind Sandstone, best exposed in Hind Clough in the Forest of Bowland area, and being similar in character to the Pendleside Sandstone.

The first major Millstone Grit sandstone of the Craven Basin is the Pendle Grit. The Pendle Grit marks the onset of the Namurian stage of the Carboniferous which was dominated by the deposition of siliciclastic material, i.e., quartz-rich sediments, which formed the Millstone Grit Group. The Millstone Grit forms may of the peaks and scarp faces which characterise the Craven and Pendle district. However, the Pendle Grit has a different character to that of the Millstone Grit which dominates the upland areas of much of the Pennines and Yorkshire Dales. The Millstone Grit Group is a thick sequence of interbedded mudstones, sandstones and coals which underlie most of Lancashire and Yorkshire either at outcrop or buried at depth. In places the Millstone Grit Group has been eroded to expose the older underlying limestones, e.g., in the Clitheroe area. The mudstones were dominantly deposited in marine conditions in low energy environments whereas most of the sandstones were deposited by high energy currents, either beneath the sea or in large river systems and deltas.

Sediment gravity currents

Before considering the Pendle Grit, and associated sedimentary rocks, it is useful to consider the types of flows which deposit marine sedimentary rocks. Most of the sandstones of the Millstone Grit have been interpreted by many workers, since the seminal petrological work of Gilligan in 1920, to have been deposited by large rivers similar to the modern day Jamuna river of Bangladesh. In contrast, the Pendle Grit, like the Mam Tor Sandstone of the Edale Basin, is considered to be a marine sedimentary rock. So how are thick accumulations of sand deposited on the sea floor?

Most of the sand carried to the coast is transported by river systems. In these environments, sand is dominantly carried as bedload, i.e., the force of the overriding flow applies a shear stress to the bed and drags, bounces and rolls the sediment downstream. This way, sedimentary features such as dunes and bars are formed. Sand then either accumulates to form deltas and beaches, or may be transported directly into deeper water through submarine canyons incised into the continental shelf (where river currents are strong and the flow density is great enough).

Well-mixed combinations of fluid and sediment, termed 'suspensions', can flow beneath less dense fluids, in this case seawater, as a consequence of their excess density. This is the same process by which pyroclastic flows (dense volcanic ash clouds) from volcanoes move along the ground, or by which cold air fronts can flow beneath warmer air. Large volume sediment suspensions may develop through collapse of large sediment deposits, such as at delta fronts or on continental slopes. In more recent times, probably the most well-known example of this was a submarine landslide generated by the Grand Banks earthquake of Newfoundland, which occurred in 1929. The earthquake triggered a landslide, mobilizing a huge volume of sediment on the continental slope. As the mass of material moved down-slope, a sediment suspension developed, which moved under the force of gravity and developed into a turbidity current, breaking telecommunications cables as it moved. In the case of the Grand Banks earthquake turbidity current, it is estimated that this single event generated a deposit with a volume of 185 cubic kilometres. The name turbidity current describes both the way in which particles in the flow are supported, i.e., by turbulent forces, but also their turbid (opaque with sediment) nature (**fig. 2**). Turbulence is random, acting in all directions, and hence the flows which can hold sediment in suspension are also able to erode the seafloor. Seafloor erosion can add more sediment to the suspension and allows the current to maintain itself for considerable distances downslope. The deposits of turbidity currents are termed 'turbidites'. For the most part, the Pendle Grit is interpreted to have been deposited by these processes.

A second class of sediment transport is also recognised from the Pendle Grit. In debris flows the sediment support mechanism is the plastic strength of the flow; these flows are said to flow in a laminar manner, with less vertical mixing than turbidity currents, and they are typically cohesive (although cohesionless debris flows can occur too). The deposits are often quite different to turbidites. Whereas turbidity currents are generally efficient sorters of sediment, and deposit well-sorted beds, debris flow deposits, or 'debrites', are often poorly-sorted, with large clasts or pebbles deposited with sand and mud. The fabric of debrites often may have a swirled or slumped appearance, and a lack of sedimentary structures such as lamination or stratification.

Pre-Pendle Grit times

The great thickness of shale known as the Lower and Upper Bowland Shale Formation records a transition from the shallow seas which dominated during deposition of the thick limestone sequences of northern England, to a period of sedimentary quiescence. Shales, or more precisely mudstones, accumulate through the settling of hemipelagic and pelagic sediment, that is, fine-grained sediment which settles over periods of months, or years. This slow process allowed the preservation of intricate details of the shells of creatures such as goniatites (ammonoids).

This period of deposition is known as 'sediment-starved', as the basin was open and 'empty'. The period of sedimentary quiescence came to an end with the arrival of the Hind Sandstone Member which is a precursor to the Pendle Grit 'proper'. The Hind Sandstone Member shares the sedimentary character of the Pendle Grit itself (discussed below), but is much thinner and very restricted in its extent. In fact, the Hind Sandstone Member is only well-developed in the Forest of Bowland area, principally at three exposures: Blue Scar, Hind Clough, and Trough Scar. The limited areal extent of this sandstone suggests that the flows which deposited it were restricted in some way, i.e., trapped between confining topography developed on the basin floor.

Although having the same character as the Pendle Grit in places, the Hind Sandstone is also unique amongst the Carboniferous sandstones. The Hind Sandstone has been affected by soft-sediment deformation, i.e., it was deformed prior to the sediment being lithified. This deformation is not like other deformation in the Millstone Grit: it takes the form of injections of sandstone into the encasing Bowland Shales. These injections are termed 'injectites' when they are preserved in the rock record. The Hind Sandstone 'injectite complex' includes upwards and downwards emplaced injectites which cross-cut the host-rock ('dykes'), and laterally emplaced, or bedding parallel injectites ('sills') (fig. 3). These are best developed at Blue Scar, where sills emanate from a large amorphous intrusion interpreted as a remobilised scour fill. Sub-vertical pipes feed into a heavily brecciated cone shaped body interpreted as a sedimentary laccolith (analogous to a volcanic laccolith). In a transect from Blue Scar, via Hind Clough to Trough Scar, the degree of deformation decreases, suggesting that the intensity of remobilisation was greatest in the Whitendale-Brennand area. The level of the Hind Sandstone is associated with slump structures in the Bowland Shale (at Calf Clough for example) (fig. 4), and it has been suggested that the injectite complex developed due to regional tectonism, developing structures such as the Sykes Anticline, that was still ongoing in early Pendleian times.

The focus at Blue Scar may reflect the presence, during deposition, of the Whitendale-Brennand Pericline (a dome shaped structural fold), onto the flanks of which the Hind Sandstones was deposited; evidence for the presence of this feature include multiple slump folds which indicate collapse in all directions off the periclines flanks (**figs. 4 & 5**).

The Pendle Grit Formation

The Pendle Grit Formation represents a sand-rich submarine channel and distributary fan complex. Submarine channels are channel systems which are found on the seafloor; in planform they often strongly resemble meandering river systems on the land. In the case of rivers, water flowing downslope cuts into the substrate to form a relatively long-lived conduit which drains the landscape. Submarine channels are thought to be formed by the flow of turbidity currents over the seafloor. These channels may flow for hundreds or even thousands of kilometers across the seafloor, and terminate in lobes or 'fans' which develop as the now unconfined flows spread out and drop their sediment load. The Upper Bowland Shales are overlain by the generally erosive base of the Pendle Grit, although this contact is not well exposed, with the exception of the excellent exposures revealed by quarrying on Waddington Fell. A complete section through the transition from the hemipelagic deposition represented by the Upper Bowland Shales to the turbulent deposition represented by the Pendle Grit is exposed on the upper parts of the flanks of Pendle Hill, particularly in Little Mearley Clough.

The arrival of the Pendle Grit.

In the Lancaster Fells Sub-Basin to the northwest, the Pendle Grit is preceded by muddy, feldspathic (i.e., rich in the mineral feldspar) sandstones. These have been termed the 'Whitendale Member' of the Pendle Grit after the Whitendale River sections, which host the 'stratotype' of this unit. The unit appears to be areally restricted to the Lancaster Fells Sub-Basin, although similar but much thinner, deposits are found in the lowest part of the succession in the northern parts of the Bowland Sub-Basin. Good exposures of the Whitendale Member are found in the Trough Scar roadside outcrops in the Forest of Bowland, and in the Whitendale and Brennand River Sections. The muddy character, together with internal deformation structures, such as slumps and slides, which indicate that the sediment was remobilised after deposition, suggest that the unit was deposited on a slope (fig. 6A).

The flows which deposited the Whitendale Member are thought to have been unable to surmount some local topography in the basin, possibly the Sykes Anticline, a tectonic deformation structure in the basin, and to have draped ('onlapped') the basin slope. As the deltaic feeder system got progressively closer, so the beds get thicker and thicker. Eventually this muddy part of the Pendle Grit gives way to the Pendle Grit proper, exposed directly above at Trough Scar, and in much larger (but less accessible) exposures at Brennand Rocks, and the surrounding tributary valleys of the Brennand and Whitendale Rivers. The first influx of turbulent currents interacted with a muddy, irregular slope, marked by significant erosion into the slope as flows attempted to create a smooth longitudinal profile, much as river systems do on land.

The very earliest deposits of the Pendle Grit exposed at Little Mearley Clough on Pendle Hill are chaotic deposits known as 'debrites' (fig. 6B). These are a mixture of sand, mud, large clasts of eroded material from the submarine slope, and anything else the flow encountered on its path. These deposits were created by debris flows – thick masses of sediment that slipped and slid down the basin slopes, moving in a plastic manner. This plastic flow behaviour is recorded in their swirled and slumped fabric and wide range of sediment sizes. Unfortunately they are poorly exposed, and are only found in the deepest parts of the exposed basin (to the south). Good examples are found at Little Mearley Clough, beneath the waterfall formed by the first major sandstones of the Pendle Grit. These thick, muddy debris flow deposits are exposed in a water worn section, however, a better section is found poking out of the adjacent hillside. Large balls of coarse-grained sandstone, and even some small limestone pebbles are found within the rock, which has a muddy matrix and convoluted fabric.

These muddy deposits are, in turn, overlain by two ~1 m thick sandstone deposits which include quartz and limestone granules and pebbles. These are also interpreted as debris flow deposits. Together these muddy and sandy debris flow deposits represent a 'switch-on' signature of the Pendle Grit system, signifying erosion of the muddy slope and formation of an erosional conduit which steered future flows into the basin.

The Pendle Grit

The erosion of the submarine slope and the cutting of a new pathway for the turbidity currents of the Pendle Grit led to the development of the debris flow deposits discussed above. Those muddy deposits give way to the Pendle Grit sandstones. The turbid suspensions of mud and sand of the Pendle Grit now experienced a smoother slope profile and thick piles of sand were deposited across the Bowland Sub-Basin. As the flows traversed the slope they deposited their sediment load. In areas closest to the palaeo-coastline, the coarsest sediment was deposited; as the flows moved down the slope, so the sand deposited became progressively finer-grained. This is revealed by looking at the Pendle Grit at a number of positions along the submarine slope profile. In the northern-most exposures, for example at Baxton Fell and Brennand Rocks, the Pendle grit is very coarse-grained and may include beds, or parts of beds, which are dominated by smooth quartz pebbles (notably at the long-disused Baxton Fell quarry) (**fig. 6C**). On Waddington Fell, the large working quarry extracts sandstone blocks for building and crushed sandstone for aggregate and sand of varying grades. At this locality, which is interpreted to have been farther down the submarine slope, the grain size has decreased, although it is still often very-coarse and includes pebbly layers (**fig. 6E & F**). Much further down the slope, at the Nick of Pendle, the Pendle Grit is medium to coarse-grained, having largely lost its pebbly component. Interaction with a topographically complex slope still occurred as illustrated by slumps with folds indicating transport between NW and NE (**fig. 6D**).

As well as the change in grain-size there is considerable variation in the shape of the sandstone bodies and individual beds which make up the Pendle Grit as the outcrops are traced down the length of the submarine slope. In the northern-most parts of the basin, i.e., in the areas closest to the original coastline, the Pendle Grit is comprised of thick sandstone beds, sometimes up to 5 metres thick (e.g., at Baxton Fell and Waddington Fell). The beds often have complex three-dimensional geometries, forming 'pod'-like shapes which stack into larger amalgamated bodies. At Waddington Fell and Longridge Fell, sandstone bodies have distinctive lenticular and sigmoidal geometries, which are often exposed in sections oblique of perpendicular to palaeoflow (**fig. 7**). These have been interpreted as channelised sandstones, in particular point bar style deposits akin to the sand bars which form at the inside of river meanders. In contrast, sandstones deeper in the basin tend to form beds which form more recognisable bedding, with interbedded mudstones, although even this far into the basin the Pendle Grit is still sand-rich (**fig. 8A**).

Perhaps one of the most distinctive features of the Pendle Grit is the presence of clasts of mudstone, which are found within sandstone beds, commonly in the upper parts, and often draping bedding planes. Where the relatively soft mudstone clasts have weathered out of the sandstones, they often leave distinctive impressions. Some of the best examples of these features are found at the Nick of Pendle and Wiswell Quarries (**fig. 8B**).

These clasts are often laminated mudstones, indicating that they were eroded somewhere upstream and transported to the place where they were deposited. The degree to which the clasts have been rounded gives a clue as to how far they were transported, for example, in the northern parts of the basin they are often angular, suggesting limited transport, whereas farther down the basin slope they tend to be more well-rounded. Some large (300 mm diameter) pale-coloured mudstone clasts have been found in Waddington Fell Quarry (**fig. 8C**); chemical analyses of these suggest that they were eroded from the land area, possibly a river floodplain or similar environment.

Flutes and Megaflutes

Flutes are a distinctive feature of turbidite sandstones; they are a type of erosional scour which is typically formed by erosion into a cohesive bed of sediment, such as mudstone. They can be preserved as a cast of the erosional scour protruding from the base of sandstone beds. They have a characteristic geometry, and are typically (in the Pendle Grit) 5-30 mm in length, 2-15 mm wide, and 2-10 mm deep. They have steeper margins on one side and flare out to the opposite end. The steeper end forms by flow separation and enhanced turbulence as the flow passes over the feature and hence these features are a reliable indicator of the direction of the currents which created them (palaeocurrents).

Megaflutes are much larger erosional features which have a similar geometry to flutes (**fig. 8A**). In terms of genesis they differ in that they are typically found within sandstone beds and are produced as the current which deposited the sand bed waxed and waned, i.e., increased and decreased in energy through time, switching from depositing sediment to eroding sediment within the same unit. More commonly, upper bedding planes are undulose and form weak flute like geometries, indicating that the bed was scoured by overriding flows but was not cohesive enough to maintain a flute-like geometry. Some of these structures are much larger than the actual outcrops themselves – for example on the lowermost bedding plane at Wiswell Quarry. Good examples are exposed at the Nick of Pendle, Brennand Rocks, Wiswell Quarry and Baxton Fell Quarry. Often these megaflutes acted as traps for very coarse-grained sediment and mudstone clasts which became 'ponded' within them.

Ripple lamination and cross stratification

In stark contrast to most of the rest of the Millstone Grit, the Pendle Grit is often devoid of sedimentary structures such as cross-bedding, and cross-lamination. These structures form by the migration of sand waves, or dunes, and smaller ripples respectively. Cross-stratification is the most-easily identifiable sedimentary structure, as it takes the form of prominent dipping surfaces marking sandstone beds; these however, are noticeably absent in the Pendle Grit. Cross-lamination, or ripple-lamination, is more common. Good exposures of ripple-lamination occur at the Nick of Pendle, Wiswell Quarry, Waddington Fell Quarry and Baxton Fell Quarry (**figs. 8D & E**). Ripple lamination is formed as sand ripples migrate under an active current. The downstream side of the ripple is preserved as the upstream side is eroded, so that sets of inclined laminations are preserved. These are important in terms of constructing the past depositional environment as they are another indicator of palaeocurrent direction. Where bedding planes are exposed, such as at Nick of Pendle, the three-dimensional shape of the dunes is revealed. From these, a more reliable estimation of the local palaeocurrent direction can be ascertained.

Loading structures

Another common feature of sandstone turbidites is loading structures. Loading structures form when a thick sand deposit is deposited on top of a non-compacted soft sediment, such as a mudstone. The sandstone will founder downwards into the mudstone to produce a distinctive bulbous morphology on the base of the sandstone bed. The mudstone is usually weathered away, but when exposed a flame-like geometry may be revealed where the mud injected upwards into the sand. Thin sandstones may also be loaded and deformed in this way. Good examples of soft-sediment loading are found throughout the Pendle Grit, but notable examples occur at the Nick of Pendle and Wiswell Quarries (**fig. 8F**).

Concretions

Large, spherical-shaped and cannonball-sized features are found throughout the Millstone Grit, and are very common within the Pendle Grit; these are termed concretions. Concretions are formed when minerals grow within the pore spaces of sedimentary rocks. This typically occurs when the rocks or sediments are buried within the Earth's crust. Fluids which flow through the pore spaces of the sediments carry with them dissolved minerals which may precipitate within the rock, often around a central nucleus, such as a fossil or large clast. The concretion grows outwards forming concentric layers, like those of an onion, and often grow to form spherical bodies. These range in size from millimeter scale to much larger features up to a metre in diameter. Quarry workers had various names for these including 'red horses', 'mares' balls', and 'doggers'. Because the mineralisation often makes the concretion less susceptible to weathering, they are often found as cannonball-like features protruding from the rock face (**fig. 8A**), or may break from the rock face during quarrying. Piles of these 'cannonballs' are found at the entrance to Wiswell Quarry and Waddington Fell Quarry. In the Pendle Grit, the concretions are formed by iron carbonate. As well as forming hard weathering features, the opposite is also true: the fluids which precipitated minerals in some parts of sandstone beds may remove the cement binding the rock in others, or replace it with a weaker cement. This leaves the rock susceptible to weathering. Rocks affected by this process often have distinctive recessively weathered faces, with quartz grains crumbling from the surface; often the rock has a distinctive yellow colouration; at Waddington Fell Quarry colours are vivid and range from yellows to reds to purples; these can clearly be seen from outside the quarry perimeter fence (open access land).

Where mineralizing fluids pass through the sedimentary rock they often leave tell-tale patterns of mineral precipitation, known as Liesegang Rings.

These are often difficult to make out on weathered outcrop faces, but are easy to spot in freshly quarried faces, and are commonly visible on many of the paving stones of our town and city centres.

Trace Fossils

Fossils fall into two types: body fossils and trace fossils. Body fossils are common in the Carboniferous limestones and some of the mudstone sequences; they form through the burial and preservation of the organism, or, more commonly, the organisms hard parts (skeletal and shell material). In sandstones, the preservation of body fossils is generally less common; this is due to a number of factors including 1) the generally high levels of oxygenation in sandy depositional environments; 2) the effects of weathering and chemical breakdown of hard-parts; and 3) the abrasion and breaking of hard parts during sediment transport, both in rivers and turbidity currents. Trace fossils are more common than body fossils in marine and fluvial sandstones of the Millstone Grit Group. Trace fossils are the preserved record of organisms burrowing, feeding and generally moving around within the sediment. They are often preserved at the interface of different sedimentary rock types, such as where sandstone overlies mudstone. Many of the trace fossils are created by worm-like creatures which had no hard parts to preserve, but left casts of their burrows behind (fig. 8G). In the area covered by this book, trace fossils within the Pendle Grit are fairly uncommon and of a low diversity. Elsewhere, greater diversities have been found, for example in the Pendle Grit exposed on the flanks of Skipton Moor (most of those samples are now kept in Keele Universities geological collections).

Examples of worm-like traces are generally limited to the areas deeper in the basin, such as at the Nick of Pendle and Wiswell Quarry, where they are found on the bases of sandstones overlying mudstones. In the northern parts of the basin, such as Waddington Fell Quarry, these trace fossils are relatively rare. The rarity and low-diversity of trace fossils here, even in sedimentologically 'quiet' environments which might otherwise be suitable for colonisation, suggests that organisms were restricted through environmental conditions, such as fluctuating salinity levels or anoxia. In the Craven Basin it is a possibility that fully marine conditions were punctuated by periods of reduced salinity due to a lack of a fully marine opening to the basin, and that truly marine conditions prevailed only at times of high sea-level. These periods are marked by full marine faunas, characterized by the widespread development of goniatite-rich horizons, appropriately known as 'marine bands'.

Subsidence vs. Tectonics

The different styles of Pendle Grit deposition are interpreted to be related to the distance from source, i.e., how far the flows have travelled into the basin, and also the local basin setting. In proximal areas, i.e., areas close to the palaeo-coastline, the basin was dominated by faulting. One of the key considerations when studying ancient sedimentary systems is the way in which the system was confined. The style of confinement influences the resultant shape of sedimentary bodies, and their distribution. For example, turbidity currents which are relatively unconfined tend to spread radially, consequently they lose momentum and their sediment load is deposited. Conversely, flows confined within a conduit (a channel), or which follow a pre-existing basin low, tend to maintain their energy and carry their sediment further. Typical sedimentary sequences in deep-marine environments where flows lack confinement are dominated by sheet-like or tabular beds of rhythmically interbedded sandstones and mudstones (for example the Mam Tor Sandstones of the Peak District); in environments where flows are confined, deposits tend to be thick amalgamations of sandstone, with a lower mud content (typical Pendle Grit facies). Geological maps of the area reveals that the Pendle Grit typically occurs in bands which are adjacent, and parallel, to local fault trends. The Pendle Grit of Waddington Fell is one such example; the sandstone has a wedge-like geometry, expanding to the north, and is dominated by large scale dipping surfaces which expand to an area of faulting. These sedimentary and tectonic features suggest the strata has built during times of active faulting and was strongly channelised. Similarly, the Pendle Grit on Skipton Moor is interpreted to have been channelised, with faults which developed synchronously with sedimentation considered to have controlled the flows which deposited the Pendle Grit (Andy Sims unpublished Ph.D. thesis, University of Leeds, 1988). Elsewhere, the Pendle Grit has a more sheet-like character, and is often subdivided by mudstone intervals. These more distal environments are considered to be at the base-of-slope and largely unaffected by the faulting which affected the basin margin.

Variscan Deformation

After the Pendle Grit had been deposited and buried by later sediments of the Millstone Grit, it was affected by a major tectonic event. The early history of the Bowland Sub-Basin, as outlined above, was dominated by extensional tectonics; the Earth's tectonic plates were pulled apart from the north and south, and these forces, combined with subsidence of the thinned crust, created the basin. Towards the end of the Carboniferous period, the tectonic forces were reversed, and the extensional regime became one of compression. The plates were pushing together, deforming the sedimentary fill of the basin by folding and faulting; this tectonic event is referred to as the Variscan Orogeny and was a period of mountain building analogous to the modern day uplift of the Himalayas, similarly caused by the collision of tectonic plates. On the largest scale, deformation was influenced by the block and basin topography, with very large folds which buckled upwards occurring within the sedimentary successions within the basins. These folds are termed 'anticlines', good examples of which are found within the successions of the Skipton area (e.g., Skipton Rock Quarry), at Waddington Fell, and in Clitheroe. The effect of the folding is that rocks in the centre of the anticlines are commonly tightly folded, whereas rocks on the flanks are more broadly folded and dip gently. This is expressed in the Craven and Pendle district by the broad arch of bedding planes which dip to the south as part of the southern limb of the anticline and to the north at Waddington Fell as part of the northern limb of the anticline. The lateral continuation of the anticline is also exposed to the east of Skipton, where rocks of Embsay Quarry generally dip to the north, and rocks of Skipton Moor dip to the south. In the core of the anticline, the older limestones and mudstones are much more tightly folded (at Skipton Rock Quarry). In contrast, carbonate platform areas, which were developed on top of the rigid block structures, remain relatively undeformed (e.g., the Askrigg Block exposed at Malham Cove and elsewhere, and the Derbyshire Massif exposed in the area to the south of Castleton in Derbyshire). Smaller tectonic features associated with the Variscan Orogeny are interpreted by some workers to have developed during the early to mid Carboniferous, for example the Whitendale-Brennand Pericline (**fig. 5**) and smaller compressional folds and faults at Waddington Fell Quarry and surrounding area (**fig. 8H**).

Conclusions

The Craven Basin developed due to extensional tectonics pulling apart the Earth's crust. Limestone deposition ceased in the deeper parts of the basin, which were now too deep and anoxic. Sediment accumulation continued through the settling of fine-grained particles from the water column, accumulating the thick Bowland Shales. This vast period of sedimentary quiescence came to a temporary halt with the first influx of coarse-grained siliciclastic sediment into the basin, which formed the Hind Sandstone. The basin was still actively deforming, perhaps through minor movements of faults, but also through some compressional activity. As a result of these tectonics, the Hind Sandstone was remobilised after it had been buried, and was injected into the surrounding rock. A relatively short spell of quiescence followed, which was interrupted by the arrival of the Pendle Grit. The Pendle Grit represents the deposits of a large submarine channel and fan system developed in the sediment starved Craven Basin. Immediately prior to the arrival of the Pendle Grit, debris flow deposits arrived in the basin, indicating some erosion of the slope into the basin. These chaotic deposits effectively 'cleared the throat' of the depositional system. The Pendle Grit itself is a coarse-grained sandstone deposited by powerful turbidity currents which were confined partly by erosion, and partly by the pre-existing topography of the basin. The evolution of the Pendle Grit depositional system and associated sedimentary units is summarised in Figure 9.

The Pendle Grit has a very different character to other Millstone Grit sandstones, and lacks the typical cross-bedding and well-developed grading that is so common within the fluvial sandstone units above. It is characterised by thick amalgamated beds, with erosional flutes and megaflutes, and lenses and layers of mudstone clasts. Perhaps due to its lack of typical sedimentary structures, the Pendle Grit has been somewhat poorly studied, however, with this description in hand, the Hind Sandstone and Pendle Grit might well be worth another look!

Acknowledgements

Dr Ole Martinsen (Statoil) in particular is thanked for instigating this study, following on from his Ph.D. work in the late 1980s under Prof. John Collinson, formerly of the University of Bergen. Prof. Bill McCaffrey (Leeds) encouraged this postdoctoral work in collaboration with the

Turbidites Research Group at Leeds. Prof. John Collinson and I co-led a field trip to the Craven Basin for the British Sedimentological Research Group in 2008, which sparked some interesting research questions. Dr Andy Sims (Merlin Energy) provided the framework for this study with his Ph.D. research at the University of Leeds on the Pendleian strata in the area, also in the late 1980s. Andy continued to support this work and even came back up north to revisit some of his old haunts, for which he is sincerely thanked. I would also like to thank the staff and managers at Waddington Fell Quarry (Aggregate Industries) for allowing me to wander round their active quarry, and on several occasions even allowing entire field groups in. I also thank Steve Donovan for his review of an earlier draft of this Chapter.

Some Useful References

Baines, J. G. (1977): The stratigraphy and sedimentology of the Skipton Moor Grits and their lateral equivalents. *Unpublished Ph.D. thesis, University of Keele, UK.*

Brandon, A., Aitkenhead, N. Crofts, R. G. Ellison, R. A. Evans D. J. and Riley, N. J. (1998): Geology of the Country around Lancaster. *Memoir of the British Geological Survey, Sheet 59 (England and Wales).*

Collinson, J. D. (1988): Controls on Namurian sedimentation in the central Province basins of northern England. *In* B. M. Besly and G. Kelling, (eds.). *Sedimentation in a synorogenic Basin complex: the Carboniferous of northwest Europe.* Glasgow, Blackie, pp. 85-101.

Gawthorpe, R. L. (1987): Tectono-sedimentary evolution of the Bowland Basin, northern England, during the Dinantian. *Journal of the Geological Society of London, 144, pp. 59–71.*

Gilligan, A. (1920): The petrography of the Millstone Grit Series of Yorkshire. *Quarterly Journal of the Geological Society, London, 75, pp. 251–294.*

Kane, I. and Collinson, J. (2008): Sedimentology and Architecture of Submarine Slope Channels: the Pendle Grit Formation (Pendleian, Carboniferous) of the Craven Basin. *Field Trip Guidebook for the British Sedimentological Research Group AGM, University of Liverpool, UK.*

Kane, I. A., McCaffrey, W. D., and Martinsen, O. J. (2009): Autogenic vs. Allogenic controls on Megaflute Formation. *Journal of Sedimentary Research, 79, pp. 643-651.*

Kane, I. A. (2010): Development and flow structures of sandstone injectites: the Hind Sandstone Member injection complex, Carboniferous, UK. *Marine and Petroleum Geology, 27, pp. 1200-1215.*

Kane, I. A., Catterall, V., McCaffrey, W. D. and Martinsen, O. J. (2010): Submarine channel response to intra-basinal tectonics. *American Association of Petroleum Geologists Bulletin, 94, pp. 189-219.*

Lee, A. G. (1988): Studies of Carboniferous Basin configuration and evolution in north and central England using gravity and magnetic data. *Unpublished Ph.D. thesis, University of Leeds, UK.*

Martinsen, O. J. (1990): Interaction between eustasy, tectonics and sedimentation with particular reference to the Namurian E1c-H2c of the Craven-Askrigg area, northern England. *Unpublished Ph.D. thesis, Geologisk Institutt Avd. A, Universitetet I Bergen.*

Martinsen, O. J. (1993): Namurian (late Carboniferous) depositional systems of the Craven-Askrigg area, northern England; implications for sequence stratigraphic models. *In* H. W. Posamentier, C. P. Summerhayes, B. U. Haq, and G. P. Allen, (eds.). Sequence Stratigraphy and Facies Associations. *International Association of Sedimentologists Special Publication 18, pp. 247-281.*

Sims, A. P. (1988): The evolution of a sand-rich basin fill sequence in the Pendleian of north-west England. *Unpublished Ph.D. thesis, University of Leeds, UK.*

FIGURE 1

(**A**) Location of the present study area, the Bowland Sub-Basin within the Craven Basin of northern England, UK. The Craven Basin is defined by the Askrigg Block and southern Lake District High at its northern margin, and the Central Lancashire High to the south. The Lancashire Fells and Bowland Sub-Basins are separated by the Bowland High, coincident with a deeper structure, the Bowland Line (figure modified from Brandon et al., 1998). NCF, MCF, SCF: North, Middle and South Craven Faults respectively.

(**B**) Structural configuration of the Bowland Sub-Basin from Mid-Late Chadian to early Pennsylvanian times. A series of NW-SE-trending transfer faults and NE-SW-trending antithetic faults, related to the Pendle Fault System, developed in response to extension during Chadian to early Arundian times, causing segmentation of the basin which had a profound impact on sedimentary facies and thickness distributions (Gawthorpe, 1987; figure also modified from Gawthorpe, 1987). PM: Pendle Monocline; WF: Waddington Fell Quarry.

(**C**) Generalized stratigraphy of the Bowland Sub-Basin.

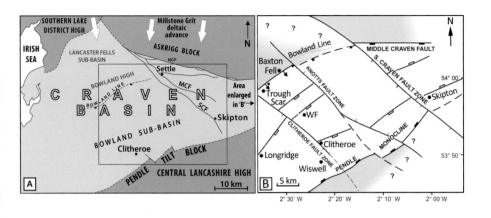

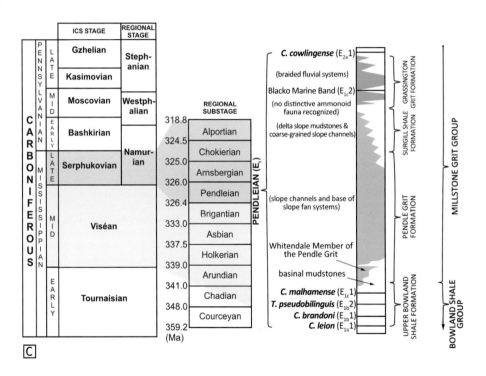

FIGURE 2

End member classes of sediment gravity flows responsible for deposition of sandstones and mudstones of the Pendle Grit and associated sedimentary rocks. Debris flows are cohesive, they flow in a laminar manner with particles supported by the matrix strength of the flow. They can be very poorly sorted, transporting clasts and grains of all sizes, from mud to large boulders. Their deposits are known as debrites and reflect their transport history by being poorly sorted and typically ungraded, with a swirled and slumped appearing fabric. Turbidity currents are fluidal flow where the particles are supported by fluid turbulence. They flow on the seafloor due to the excess density of the grains and interstitial fluid, which together are more dense than the surrounding seawater. Turbidity currents are efficient sorters of sediment, and the deposits reflect this, often being graded and having a reactively narrow grain size range.

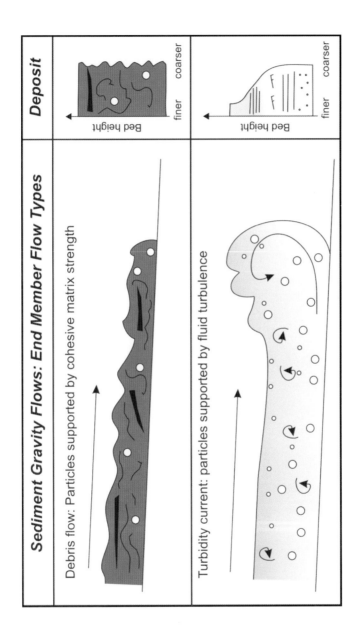

Sediment Gravity Flows: End Member Flow Types

	Deposit

Debris flow: Particles supported by cohesive matrix strength

Turbidity current: particles supported by fluid turbulence

Bed height — finer — coarser

Bed height — finer — coarser

FIGURE 3

Blue Scar

(A) Amorphous sandstone body interpreted as a remobilised gully-fill. The sand body feeds into several sills, most of which are not laterally continuous on the scale of the outcrop. Note the effect of differential compaction on the underlying sills.

(B) A dyke that injected upwards into a sill complex, forming a conical body with a chaotic to blocky fabric, which feeds into various sills and was even injected back downwards into the Upper Bowland Shales. The dyke appears to have met some resistance at this level and has remobilised partly cemented sediment, resulting in the blocky nature of the conical body; this feature is termed a sedimentary laccolith. The overlying sandstones are jacked-up by the intrusion giving the complex of sandstones a mounded appearance.

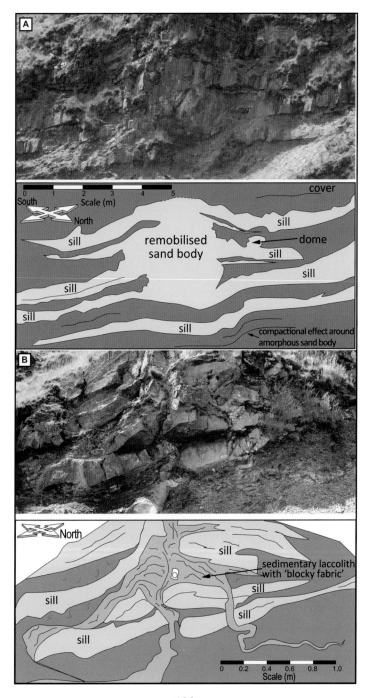

FIGURE 4

Calf Clough

Syn-sedimentary slump within the Upper Bowland Shales at the stratigraphic level of the HSM. This location is approximately 800 m to the north-east of Blue Scar (highlighted in the distance). The HSM is reduced to two thin sandstones at this locality. The direction of slumping (120°) indicates movement down the flank of the Whitendale-Brennand Pericline, approximately the reverse of regional palaeoflow, indicating that the pericline was a seafloor feature during the deposition of the Hind Sandstone; a number of slumps shed from the flanks of the feature suggest that the pericline was active during the Pendleian.

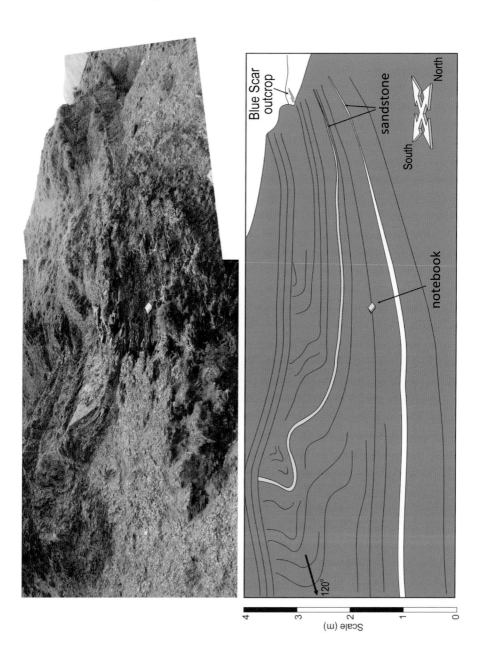

Blue Scar outcrop

sandstone

North

South

notebook

120°

Scale (m)
4
3
2
1
0

FIGURE 5

Pendleian sedimentation in the Whitendale-Brennand area over the Whitendale-Brennand pericline (a structural dome superimposed on the larger Sykes anticline).

(**A**)   Growth of the Sykes Anticline commenced during Viséan times (Fig. 1), the structure was draped by the dominantly hemipelagic Bowland Shales, but continued to be active. The Hind Sandstone Member was deposited in shallow laterally restricted slope gullies and scours.

(**B**)   The structure continued to grow and was onlapped by the Whitendale Member turbidites and debrites of the Pendle Grit. The Pendle Grit was deposited as a sand-rich channelised slope fan.

(**C**)   Migration of basinal fluids, including hydrocarbons, along fractures and faults associated with the basin margin, underlying structures and the Sykes anticline. Fluids migrated along fractures in the Upper Bowland Shales, locally brecciating the unit. Fluids are interpreted to have passed into the Hind Sandstone gully and scour fills, generating significant overpressure.

(**D**)   The Hind Sandstone Member becomes remobilised through some combination of tectonism associated with the growing anticline and differential loading over the anticline/pericline. The focus of remobilisation was in the vicinity of the Whitendale-Brennand Pericline, which coincides with the location of the most significant mineralisation within the underlying limestones.

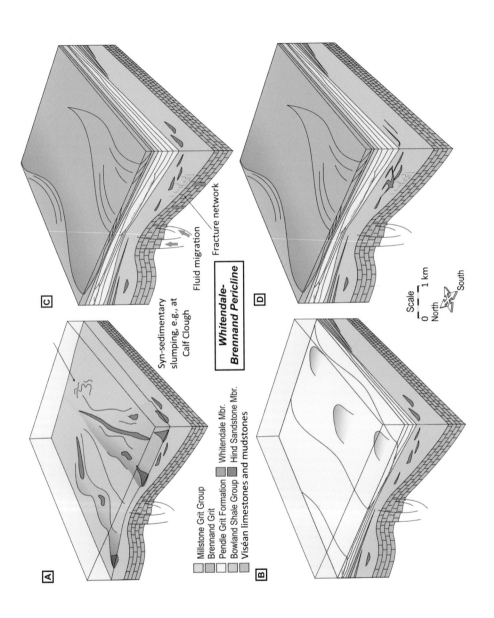

A

B

C

Syn-sedimentary
slumping, e.g., at
Calf Clough

Fluid migration

Fracture network

D

*Whitendale-
Brennand Pericline*

Millstone Grit Group
Brennand Grit
Pendle Grit Formation
Whitendale Mbr.
Bowland Shale Group
Hind Sandstone Mbr.
Viséan limestones and mudstones

Scale
0 ─── 1 km

North
South

- 124 -

FIGURE 6

(**A**)   Folded bedding within a slump of the Whitendale Member part of the Pendle Grit Formation. The orientation of the fold hinge indicates movement of the slump towards the north. Location: Brennand River section.

(**B**)   Debris flow deposit (debrite) of mudstone and sandstone. Note the large very coarse grained sandstone balls in the centre and middle right of the photo. Tape Measure for scale. Location: Waterfall beneath Pendle Grit at Little Mearley Clough.

(**C**)   Rounded quartz pebbles in the proximal Pendle Grit at Baxton Fell End Quarry.

(**D**)   Slump within the Pendle Grit. Note the deformed and non-bedded nature of the sandstone here, compared to typical Pendle Grit. This slump again indicates movement towards the north. Location: Top of Swine Clough, near to Brennand Rocks.

(**E**) & (**F**)   Cut blocks of the Pendle Grit at Waddington Fell Quarry revealing the normally-graded nature of the bedding (fining upwards from granular and pebbly to medium-grained). The bed is truncated by an erosion surface just above the shale clasts in the upper part of bed; this is enlarged in 'F'.

(**F**)   Nature of the erosion surface in 'E'; note the very fresh, pink-coloured feldspars, which are generally too weathered in outcrop to be visible.

FIGURE 7

Waddington Fell Quarry

(**A**) Large-scale lateral accretion deposits. A thick mudstone-clast breccia drapes one of the lateral accretion deposits, and is developed in a scour eroded into the top of the body. To the right of the image the thick amalgamated sandstone which characterizes axial deposits is transitional with more tabular beds.

(**B**) Stratigraphically beneath 'A', this outcrop features lateral accretion surfaces draped by mudstone clasts, with a thin sandstone developed over the top, and loaded at its base. Another mudstone clast breccia overlies the sandstone. Note Dr. Andy Sims for scale.

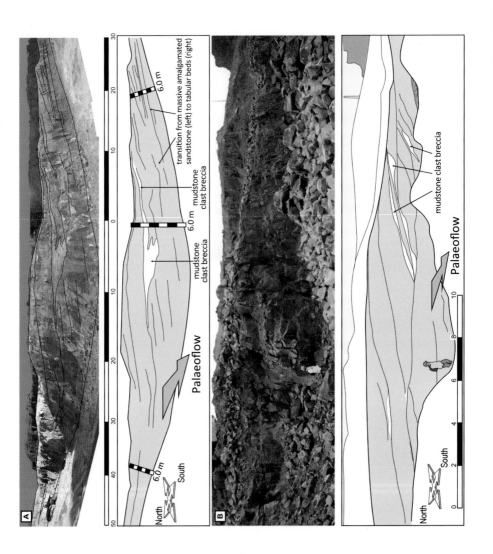

FIGURE 8

(**A**)   Megaflute on top of a bedding plane at the upper Wiswell Quarry (topographically higher but stratigraphically lower). Note the thick amalgamated sandstone beds and prominent concretion to the middle right, which has formed in a smaller megaflute structure. Professor Bill McCaffrey for scale.

(**B**)   Casts of mud clasts deposited on a turbidite bedding plane. The clasts are soft and have weathered away, leaving imprints revealing that they were relatively well-rounded, suggesting a   relatively long transport distance. Location: upper Wiswell.

(**C**)   Large pale-grey to pink clay clasts at the base of the Pendle Grit. These are kaolinitic indicating direct input from a kaolin source onshore.

(**D**)   Ripple-forms preserved on top of a bedding plane. These ripples indicate flow approximately from right to left in the photo. Flask for scale (300 mm tall). Location: central Nick of Pendle quarry.

(**E**)   Thin ripple forms preserved within mudstone and siltstone. Note the cross lamination of these features, with foresets dipping to the right and indicating palaeoflow in approximately that direction (south west).

(**F**)   Loaded bed base; these bulbous loading structures indicate that the underlying mudstone was soft when the turbidite bed above was deposited. Location: northernmost Nick of Pendle quarry.

(**G**)   Trace fossils on the base of a turbidite bed at Waddington Fell Quarry respectively. These represent simple worm like burrow casts formed at the interface of turbidite sandstones and hemipelagic mudstones.

(**H**)   Syn-sedimentary and post-depositional faulting is common at Waddington Fell Quarry. This fault has deformed the bedding into a monoclinal structure; the sediment was still soft at the time of deformation as it has been injected into the underlying mudstones in places.

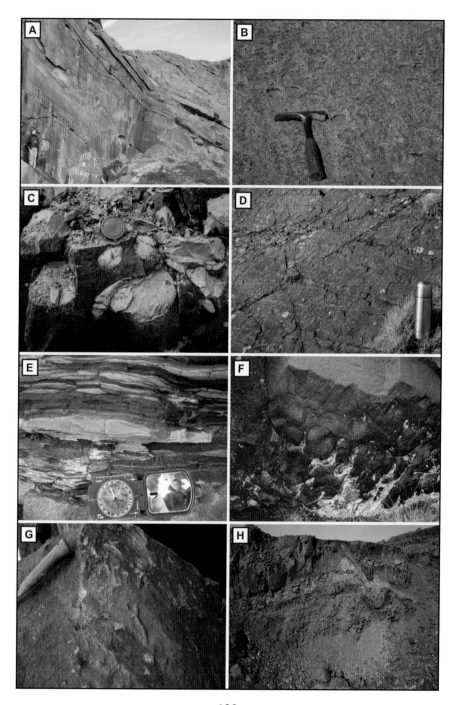

FIGURE 9

Summary model for the development of the Pendle Grit Formation in the Craven and Pendle district.

(A)   Hemipelagic mud deposition during times of dominantly high sea-levels (although these fluctuated), over the top of the buried limestones; the accumulated muds form the Upper Bowland Shales.

(B)   Lowered sea-level coincides with the influx of turbidite sands which form the Hind Sandstone Member.

(C)   A hiatus of high energy deposition, and continued deposition of the Upper Bowland Shales.

(D)   Whitendale Member of the Pendle Grit is deposited in, and restricted to, the Lancaster Fells Sub-Basin.

(E)   Hiatus and deposition of mudstone interval.

(F)   The Pendle Grit system arrives, again interpreted to correspond to sea-level lowstand conditions. Sediment transport and deposition is strongly controlled by intra-basinal faults. To the north the depositional system is strongly channelised, to the south it has a slightly more lobate geometry.

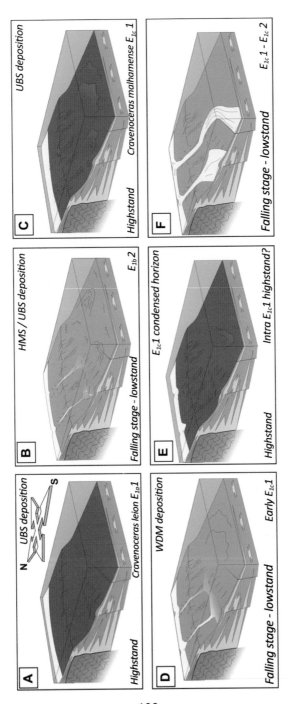

A   N   S   UBS deposition

Highstand   Cravenoceras leion $E_{1a}1$

B   HMS / UBS deposition

Falling stage - lowstand $E_{1b}2$

C   UBS deposition

Highstand   Cravenoceras malhamense $E_{1c}1$

D   WDM deposition

Falling stage - lowstand   Early $E_{1c}1$

E $E_{1c}1$ condensed horizon

Highstand   Intra $E_{1c}1$ highstand?

F

Falling stage - lowstand $E_{1c}1$ - $E_{1c}2$

Chapter 5

Field Excursions

Warning: Field trip leaders and casual visitors should be aware that most of the localities are on private land so prior permission to visit should be sought from the appropriate landowner e.g., the Duchy of Lancaster, United Utilities, Chatsworth Estate, or land-owners / farm tenants. The Countryside Code and any local bye-laws should be observed at all times, and, ideally, the *Geological Fieldwork Code* should be read. The Geologists' Association carry copies of the Code available for download at www.geologistsassociation.org.uk. Alternatively, write to: Geologists' Association, Burlington House, Piccadilly, London W1J 0DU, and enclose a stamped addressed envelope with your request.

Fieldwork can be hazardous so make sure you have boots or stout footwear, and suitable clothing to cope with changes in the weather. A hard hat, high-visibility jacket and safety glasses may be required when entering a quarry. It is the responsibility of both individuals and field leaders to assess the risks involved in visiting any of the localities. Those visiting any of the sites described do so entirely at their own risk. Collecting specimens bestows a certain responsibility on the collector. You may collect a specimen of great importance. Ideally you should record where it came from and any other details thus ensuring the full scientific value of your find. Please refrain from indiscriminate hammering at featured localities. Localities which are also Sites of Special Scientific Interest (SSSI) are designated to conserve our geological heritage, and protect natural habitats e.g., Salthill Quarry Geology Trail which is both an SSSI and a Local Nature Reserve.

Some useful maps
O.S. Outdoor Leisure 41 Forest of Bowland & Ribblesdale.
O.S. Explorer Map (1:25 000) Yorkshire Dales: S & W areas Sheet OL2.
1:25 000 sheet SD 64 / 74 (Clitheroe and Chipping).

Geological Survey 1:63 360 Sheet 68 Solid Clitheroe.
Geological Survey 1:50 000 Sheet 67 Solid and Drift Garstang.
Geological Survey 1:50 000 Sheet 60 Solid and Drift Settle.

Sykes Anticline

Purpose

The broad aim of this excursion is to examine the Hetton Beck Limestone turbidite (Hodder Mudstone Formation) and the Hind Sandstone (Bowland Shale Formation).

West Sykes Quarry and Trough Scar form the morning part of the excursion. Visitors could meet at Dunsop Bridge car park [SD 661 501] where there are toilet facilities. From here proceed by car to a lay-by at Langden Brook [SD 633 512] 3 km from Dunsop Bridge where there is plenty of parking space, and in the summer months there is usually a refreshments van. Car parking is also possible 0.75 km further along Trough Road by Losterdale Brook [SD 629 517] leaving 200 m to walk to locality 1. Permission to enter should be sought from Sykes Farm, Trough Road, Dunsop Bridge BB7 3BJ.

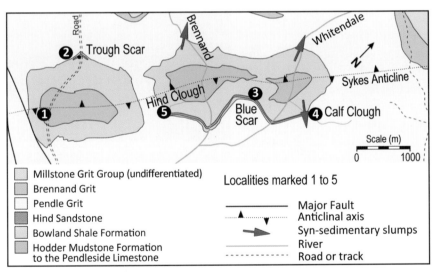

Fig. 1 Generalised stratigraphy of the area. The outcrop pattern is dominated by the approximately northeast-southwest trending Sykes Anticline. The five localities are: **1** West Sykes Quarry, **2** Trough Scar, **3** Blue Scar, **4** Calf Clough and **5** Hind Clough. The geological map of the area has been modified from British Geological Survey mapping. After Ian Kane, Statoil ASA (Research Centre), Bergen, Norway.

Locality 1   West Sykes Quarry [SD 627 519]

The quarry exposes 85 m of Hetton Beck Limestone which forms the core of Sykes Anticline (fig. 24 p. 33). It is entirely surrounded by younger rocks making it an inlier. The limestone is a fine- to coarse-grained packstone with thin shaly mudstone interbeds. Graded bedding and sharp erosive bases are features you might expect to see in limestone that was deposited as a turbidite. In the higher part of the quarry cherts appear as discreet units. Chert is a sedimentary rock which is believed to have originated from silica derived radiolarian and sponge spicules. Fossils are abundant at certain horizons, the most common being crinoids, bryozoans, ammonoids, and brachiopods. Corals are abundant, especially the large tabulate *Syringopora* colonies, and solitary rugose corals. Fossil corals are easy to see due to their selective silicification and weathering; this is especially true of *Syringopora*. The coral colonies are not preserved in growth position, and there is soft-sediment slumping to the north of the main quarry face (fig. 2). These two factors also support the view that the Hetton Beck Limestone was gravity-fed into the Bowland Sub-Basin.

Fig. 2   Hetton Beck Limestone in West Sykes Quarry. Note the intra-formational slump by the hammer.

Adits made by lead miners perhaps as long ago as 1768 are visible high up in the sequence. Common minerals found in the scree include galena, barytes, quartz, fluorspar and sphalerite.

From locality 1 to locality 2 it is approximately 1.5 km. There is limited car parking in a roadside lay-by at the entrance to the Trough of Bowland [SD 626 526]. From this lay-by it is a short walk of about 350 m to locality 2 along a stretch of road that twists and turns and can be quite busy.

Locality 2   Trough Scar [SD 625 528]

The section in Trough Scar exposes hemipelagic mudstones of the Bowland Shale Formation which accumulated in moderately deep water. During periods of high salinity marine bands were formed. The top of the section marks the first major input of sandstone into the basin; in this case from the Pendle Grit turbidite system.

The outcrops on the west bank of the stream are predominantly interbedded shales, calcareous mudstones, siltstones, and sandstones, with siderite concretions present at a few horizons. Fully marine conditions are marked by marine bands which are commonly dominated by a diagnostic thick shelled ammonoid fauna. The oldest marine band is the Tumulites pseudobilingue marine band which is exposed about 42 m below the base of the Pendle Grit. The Cravenoceras malhamense marine band is the youngest and is exposed approximately 14 m below the Pendle Grit. The Hind Sandstone (after Hind Clough in the Brennand valley) lies between the two marine bands and is exposed on both sides of the road. The sandstone is coarse-grained and feldspathic, and has a chaotic and blocky fabric, quite different from the Hind Sandstone exposed at Blue Scar and Hind Clough.

Fig. 3   View from the Trough of Bowland looking south towards Totridge Fell which is capped by Pendle Grit. In the foreground Bowland Shales underlie the bracken. The Hetton Beck Limestone in West Sykes Quarry is visible to the right of the road in the centre of the photograph.

Return to Dunsop Bridge car park [SD 661 501]. For localities 3, 4 and 5 there is an initial walk of 6 km to Whitendale Farm. In view of the distance to walk I would recommend visiting Blue Scar and Calf Clough. Including Hind Clough would make the total walking distance about 18 km!

It may be possible to obtain a permit for parking in Dunsop valley by contacting the United Utilities Bowland Estate Ranger, Bowland Estate Office, Catlow Road, Slaidburn BB7 3AQ. Tel: 01200 454414. The permit form can also be found at www.unitedutilities.com/Recreationpermits.aspx. A permit would make a visit to Hind Clough, Blue Scar and Calf Clough a feasible proposition for a one day excursion.

From Dunsop Bridge car park walk past the cafe and take the track on the right before the bridge. After 1 km pass through a farm and cross the footbridge onto the private road to Whitendale. Beyond Foot Holme the road divides [SD 653 536] with the left fork going to Brennand Farm and locality 5 (Hind Clough). Take the right fork to Whitendale. At Whitendale cross the bridge in front of the farmhouse and a footbridge on the left to take the steep track up the hillside. After a climb of 100 m you reach a stile in a wall but do not cross it. At the wall take an unmarked route due south across rough grassland for 250 m to reach Blue Scar. Approaching the face of Blue Scar may prove hazardous due to loose shale underfoot.

Locality 3   Blue Scar [SD 656 546]
Unlike Trough Scar, the Hind Sandstone at Blue Scar has been affected by soft-sediment deformation prior to the sediment being lithified. This makes the Hind Sandstone unique when compared to other Carboniferous sandstones. The deformation takes the form of injections of sandstone into the Bowland Shale Formation. The term 'dyke' is used where the Hind Sandstone cross-cuts the host-rock. Where the sandstone is laterally emplaced parallel to the bedding plane, the injectite is referred to as a 'sill'. Here at Blue Scar the sills emanate from a large amorphous sand intrusion interpreted as a remobilised scour fill.

Return to Whitendale via the same route to reach locality 4. At Whitendale take the track leading east through the farm. Calf Clough is located in the narrow valley 300 m ahead.

Locality 4 Calf Clough [SD 663 550]

The Hind Sandstone at this locality is restricted to two thin beds which are situated within a 2 m thick syn-sedimentary slump horizon in the Bowland Shale Formation. The disturbance in the shales is probably related to growth/movement on the Sykes Anticline.

For locality 5 return to Whitendale and walk back to the road junction to take the road to Brennand Farm. Walk 1 km to Brennand Farm and take the track immediately after the farm (marked Ouster Rake on the 1:25 000 map). Cross the wall [SD 642 535] into Open Access Land and, keeping at roughly the same height, head southeast across rough grassland for 350 m to reach locality 5 at Hind Clough.

Locality 5 Hind Clough [SD 644 533]

Hind Clough, the type locality for the Hind Sandstone, exposes a complex series of sills and dykes, although perhaps not as dramatic in appearance as those at Blue Scar. The likely reason for this is that the Hind Sandstone here represents a transition from depositional to fully injected sand bodies. The bases and tops of sills are generally sharp but sometimes undulate.

Fig. 4 The Hind Sandstone in Hind Clough is encased in Bowland Shale. The sills are the dominant feature whilst dykes are harder to see. A good example of a dyke to the right of the hammer is illustrated in the inset photo © Ian Kane, Statoil (Research Centre). Here the dyke connects two sills. The camera lens cap for scale.

Return to Brennand Farm and take the road back to Dunsop Bridge, a distance of about 5 km.

As an alternative itinerary you may like to consider localities 1 and 2 and then take the footpath labelled Ouster Rake from the north side of Trough Barn [SD 628 522] via Rams Clough to Hind Clough, a return distance of about 5 km.

Excursion 2

Slaidburn Anticline

Purpose

The aim of this excursion is to demonstrate a range of depositional environments from platform/ramp limestones (Tournaisian stage) to basinal hemipelagic mudstones (Viséan stage).

Background

Slaidburn is an attractive village set on the banks of the Hodder river. The village hall houses displays, artefacts, and an audio-visual presentation about the village's heritage and the Forest of Bowland. During the excursion you will see Hammerton Hall, a large three gabled building built with a layout resembling a capital letter 'E'. This was a floor-plan often used in houses built or altered during the 16th or early 17th centuries. It was once the home of the 'de Hamerton' family, a wealthy medieval family who are reputed to have been able to ride from Slaidburn to York (roughly 90 km) on their own land! This fact is illustrated by the place-names Kirk Hammerton and Green Hammerton near York, both villages being owned at one time by the family.

Locality 1   Chatburn Limestone, New Biggin Quarry [SD 690 525]

This is a disused quarry situated 3 km from Slaidburn village centre. From the Hark to Bounty pub in the village, drive along the road via Townend/Shay Lane/Woodhouse Lane. Eventually you come to a fork in the road where you take a left turn into Back Lane. Beyond Laythams Cottages, a classic example of a 17th century 'Pennine Longhouse', park on the grassy roadside verge between the two barns further along the road. The quarry is adjacent to Eller Beck and can be reached via one of two farm gates. Permission to enter should be sought from Laythams Cottages.

New Biggin Quarry is located on the northwest limb of the Slaidburn Anticline and exposes 23.5 m of Chatburn Limestone. The limestone is composed of planar- to wavy-bedded, medium to dark grey packstones and wackestones, often separated by muddy partings. There are some shelly and crinoidal limestones along with occasional chert lenses. Between the road and the quarry the geological map shows the overlying Thornton Limestone,

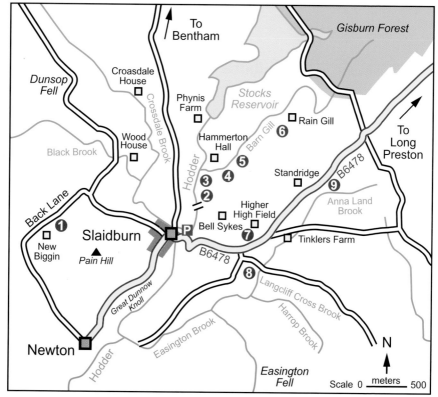

Fig. 1 Sketch map showing the approximate position of localities 1 to 9 around Slaidburn. The main visitors car park is marked on the map close to the Hodder bridge on the B6478.

however, the transition between these two limestone units is not easy to identify in the field. From locality 1 return to Slaidburn and park at the pay and display car park. Walking distance for localities 2 - 8 is about 11 km. Locality 9 is 3.5 km by car to the lay-by at Anna Land End.

Locality 2   Bellman Limestone, Hammerton Crag [SD 7180 5320]
Permission to visit the Crag should be sought from Horn Farm in Slaidburn village centre. From the car park turn right along Chapel Street. Stay on this road until you reach the Cenotaph where you turn right into The Skaithe (signposted for Bentham). At the road bridge over Croasdale Brook cross the stile onto farm land. On the opposite side of the brook by the bridge you will notice gently dipping Thornton Limestone. Follow the right of

- 141 -

way as shown on the O.S. map for approximately 500 m until you come to the River Hodder at Holmehead Bridge. Immediately over the bridge Hammerton Crag can be seen in the second field approximately 230 m east.

Hammerton Crag (fig.2) is situated on the southeast limb of the Slaidburn Anticline. The anticline was actively being formed during the deposition of these limestones at Hammerton Crag. The Crag is composed of 15 m of massive to well-bedded, medium light grey wackestones, with occasional mudstone partings. The limestone is richly crinoidal and on careful examination geopetal infills may be observed. The geological literature suggests that Hammerton Crag is composed of either Coplow Limestone or Bellman Limestone. However, fossils collected from here by Jeremy Savill of Craven & Pendle Geological Society are comparable with the fossils associated with Salthill Quarry on the adjacent Clitheroe Anticline making this locality Bellman Limestone in age.

Approximately 20 m southwest of the main part of the outcrop, wackestones at the base of Hammerton Crag rest with angular unconformity on Thornton Limestone. In the summer months the junction of the unconformity may be hidden by nettles as illustrated in the photograph below. The unconformity was first identified by R. S. Arthurton (BGS) in the late 1980s.

Fig.2   The angular unconformity between the sub-horizontal Bellman Limestone and the gently dipping Thornton Limestone at Hammerton Crag, Slaidburn. The hammer for scale stands upright on a limestone bed about 2 m higher in the sequence.

Locality 3   Thornton Limestone, Hammerton Ford, [SD 717 535]

Return to the footpath alongside the Hodder river and proceed for 500 m to Barn Gill. Between the path and the waterfall the Thornton Limestone is exposed in a small disused quarry. The limestone is typical of the upper part of the Thornton Limestone being composed of wavy-bedded to lenticular, medium dark grey packstones and wackestones.

Locality 4   Phynis Mudstone, Barn Gill [SD 721 535]

Localities in Barn Gill and Rain Gill require permission to enter from Myttons Farm, Woodhouse Lane, Slaidburn. Follow Barn Gill for about 300 m and in a meander bend of the stream look for an outcrop of blocky mudstones. The Phynis Mudstone directly overlies limestones seen earlier at Hammerton Crag. These mudstones are referable to the 'Phynis Shales' of Parkinson (1936). In Barn Gill they are micaceous, silty, calcareous mudstones, interbedded with laminated blocky siltstones. Trilobites have also been collected from this locality. The Phynis Mudstones in Phynis Beck about 1.5 km northwest of Barn Gill are much more fossiliferous, although the outcrop is not as accessible in summer due to dense vegetation cover.

Fig. 3   Phynis Mudstone outcrop at locality 4 in Barn Gill, Slaidburn. The dark mudstones are fragile making fossil collecting a challenge. Hammer for scale.

Locality 5   Whitemore Limestone, Barn Gill [SD 723 538]

Follow Barn Gill upstream for a further 200 m and keep a look out for the conformable transition from Phynis Mudstone into Whitemore Limestone. This limestone is a fine- to coarse-grained bioclastic calcareous mudstone turbidite which has yielded a rich fauna including complete carapaces of the trilobite *Gitara* sp. and the ammonoids *Ammonellipsites* and *Eonomismoceras*.

Locality 6   Rain Gill Limestone, Rain Gill [SD 728 542]

Return to Hammerton Ford and then continue along the path past Hammerton Hall but make sure you keep to the right when the path divides. Walking distance from Hammerton Ford to Rain Gill is about 1.4 km. This disused quarry is the type locality of the Rain Gill Limestone (fig. 4). The outcrop consists of 5 m of mainly fine- to coarse-grained dark grey wackestones and packstones. Slump folds are well displayed and support the view that the Rain Gill Limestone were gravity-fed into the basin (fig. 28, p. 36). The sheltered nature of the quarry would make a fine lunch stop.

Fig. 4   The disused Rain Gill Limestone quarry is 0.5 km from Rain Gill. Slump folds are particularly well developed at the southern end of the quarry where the geologist appears to be saluting the rocks!

Locality 7   Pendleside Limestone, Higher High Field [SD 726 525]

Return to Holmehead Bridge and from there take the path via Bell Sykes to Higher High Field Farm. Walking distance is about 3 km with a gentle ascent of 80 m from the bridge to the farm.

The Pendleside Limestone (fig. 31, p. 40) is widespread throughout the basin and shows considerable variation in thickness and proportion of limestone to mudstone. In the disused quarry at Higher High Field there is 10 m of Pendleside Limestone, however, the main outcrop is partially covered by vegetation. The limestone is dark grey, well-bedded and well jointed, with some beds having erosive bases. Cherts occur as discreet bodies of lensoid sheets which are parallel and sub-parallel to the bedding. Comparable sections through the Pendleside Limestone can be seen in the Lothersdale area (Excursion 6) and near Rylstone (Excursion 7).

Locality 8   Bowland Shale, Langcliff Cross Brook [SD 728 517]

Permission to visit the outcrop is required from Whiteholme Farm, Slaidburn village. Leave Higher High Field and continue along the farm track to the B6478. Turn right towards Slaidburn and after 400 m turn left along an unnamed road for 150 m. At the junction turn left and follow this road for 450 m to Langcliff Cross Brook. When you reach the bridge the outcrop is on your right. There is a farm gate about 75 m beyond the bridge with space for one or two cars only. The total walking distance from Higher High Field is about 1.6 km.

The dark organic-rich Bowland Shales in Langcliff Cross Brook are well exposed along the brook in cliff sections up to about 4 m high in places. The fossiliferous shales (fig.33, p.41) have yielded two important zonal ammonoids; *Arnsbergites falcatus* (formerly *Goniatites falcatus*) and *Paraglyphioceras elegans* (formerly *Goniatites elegans*). Other fossils found here include trilobites and a variety of bivalves. Some of the shale cliffs are unstable so care is needed when looking for fossils.

From Langcliff Cross Brook there are two options: a) return to Slaidburn village car park along the B6478 or b) take a more scenic route by crossing the B6478 and following the footpath back to Higher High Field. Look out for another footpath [SD 726 525] that takes you down the hill via Mellows to the Hodder bridge.

Locality 9   Pendleside Sandstone, Anna Land End [SD 740 533]

From Slaidburn village car park drive 3.5 km to Anna Land End. Directly opposite the farm is a lay-by offering plenty of parking.

The Pendleside Sandstone is exposed in the field between the lay-by and the farm house, and also behind the wall on the northern side of the farm. The sandstone often gives rise to prominent bench and scarp features. It is a thin- to thick-bedded, fine-grained, friable and micaceous sandstone, with platy weathering at the top.

Waddington Fell and the Ashnott Anticline

Purpose

This excursion focuses on the lower part of the Pendle Grit at Waddington Fell Quarry, and the limestone, mineralisation, and hemipelagic mudstones associated with the Ashnott Anticline.

Waddington Fell Quarry (fig.1) is an active quarry on the summit of Waddington Fell 6 km to the north of Clitheroe. There is ample parking near the entrance to the quarry by the cattle grid [SD 719 481] as marked on the map below. I recommend arranging a tour of the quarry by contacting the quarry manager. The address and telephone number is Waddington Fell Quarry, Slaidburn Road, Waddington, Clitheroe, Lancashire BB7 3AA. Tel: 01200 446334. If you choose not to arrange a visit, localities 1 and 2 on the map will provide an overview of the Pendle Grit. I recommend you consult Chapter 4 by Ian Kane on the Pendle Grit before you start the excursion.

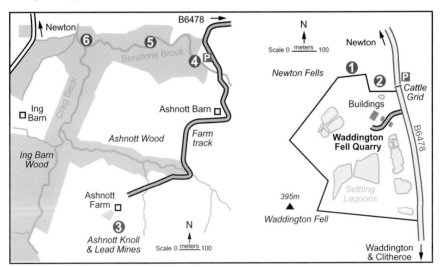

Fig. 1   A combined sketch map of Waddington Fell Quarry and Ashnott showing all the localities and parking places for the excursion. Sheep along the roadside from Waddington Fell Quarry to the farm track which leads to Bonstone Brook are a potential hazard for motorists.

Locality 1   Pendle Grit, Waddington Fell Quarry [SD 717 481]

From the viewpoint the key exposure in the quarry is the northwest slope which is about 40 m high and 400 m in length. The quarried interval consists of massive medium- to coarse-grained arkosic sandstones with subordinate mudstone drapes. The sandstones are interpreted as being deposited from high-concentration turbidity currents directly from suspension. Associated with the amalgamated sandstone beds are sigmoidal sandstone bodies together with pods of thick mudstone clast breccias which testify to a high-density turbidity current origin. The Pendle Grit overlies mudstones of the Bowland Shale Formation which crop out at the south-western end of the quarry, though not visible from the view-point.

Fig. 2   General view looking north across Waddington Fell Quarry. The building in the background is where the Pendle Grit is processed. Computerised equipment is used to ensure accurate sawing for a variety of masonry purposes, such as mullions, quoins, fireplaces and new build.

Locality 2   Pendle Grit, Waddington Fell Quarry [SD 7180 4805]

From the viewpoint at locality 1 return to the car park via a small disused quarry of Pendle Grit where you can examine samples of the sandstone. The quarry floor is partially covered with sandstone boulders so care is needed when investigating the outcrop. There are approximately 10 m of sub-horizontal amalgamated beds of fine- to coarse-grained sandstone. One of the undulose bedding planes has a pock-marked surface which shows where shale clasts have weathered out.

Please note: at localities 4, 5 and 6 in Bonstone Brook there is a commercial enterprise requiring supervision of a gamekeeper. Permission to visit the localities may be granted between February and July. Enquiries should be made through the land agent: Ingham & Yorke, Standen Estate Offices, Littlemoor, Clitheroe BB7 1HG. Tel: 01200 423655

Return to your car and continue along the road towards Newton for 1.9 km. As you drive down the fell there is another cattle grid to cross. Shortly after the cattle grid at the first sharp bend on the road (Blue Gates on the O.S. map), carefully take the farm track on the left towards New Laithe Farm. The track eventually turns sharply south towards Bonstone Brook. Park on the grass adjacent to the farm track on the north bank of the stream. After a period of inclement weather, car parking by Bonstone Brook for the afternoon session might need to be reassessed. Alternative though limited parking is possible due west of Bonstone Brook [SD 689 487].

Locality 3   Ashnott Knoll, Coplow Limestone [SD 693 481]
From Bonstone Brook follow the invariably muddy farm track to Ashnott Farm and seek permission to visit the outcrop. The limestone knoll is directly behind the farm. Walking distance from the car parking area is about 800 m.

The axis of the northeast trending Ashnott Anticline passes through Crag Wood and Ashnott Knoll. The knoll (fig. 13 p. 21) is composed of Coplow Limestone and is well exposed on the western side facing Ashnott farm. The limestone consists of 100 m of pale- to medium-grey bioclastic packstones and grainstones and is extensively fractured and jointed (fig. 3). Fossils are abundant and include a variety of brachiopods, gastropods, corals and trilobites. Small amounts of lead found on Ashnott Knoll date back to the early 19th century. There are traces of 5 shallow shafts and one adit into the knoll. The source of the mineralisation is probably associated with the expulsion of fluids from the hemipelagic mudstones during deep burial, whilst under tectonic stress, at the onset of the Variscan orogeny.

Return to the car, cross the gamekeeper's stile, and make your way to Bonstone Brook. Hiking boots or wellingtons are essential to access the outcrops. As you work your way downstream to the confluence of Bonstone Brook with Crag Beck, the Hodder Mudstones get progressively younger.

Fig. 3 Members of Craven & Pendle Geological Society looking for fossils in a hollow on Ashnott Knoll which was probably created by lead miners.

Locality 4   Rain Gill Limestone [SD 6955 4868]

Once you have reached Bonstone Brook, follow the bed of the brook upstream for a short distance. The Rain Gill Limestone is well exposed on the north bank. Look out for slump folds of dark grey to black wackestones. Carefully make your way downstream observing the numerous outcrops of mudstone until you arrive at a spectacular pseudotectonic feature.

Locality 5   Gravity Slide [SD 6953 4874]

Deposition of the Hodder Mudstones occurred at the time when the Bowland Sub-Basin had fractured into a series of basinal 'highs' and 'lows'. Ashnott developed as a basinal high point with the Hodder Mudstones onlapping against it. At locality 5 the steeply dipping mudstones appear to have been tilted by earth movements, however, in this case, the change in dip is a result of contemporaneous gravity sliding (down palaeoslope) (fig. 4, p. 150). Gravity slides occur today in a variety of environments for a number of reasons e.g., in response to an earth tremor.

Locality 6   Dunbarella Bed [SD 6917 4876]

The Dunbarella Bed is 0.2 m thick and is exposed at the confluence of Bonstone Brook and Crag Beck. It is composed of dark fissile calcareous mudstones which also contain wackestone nodules which geologists refer to as 'bullions'. The bed is crowded with the bivalves *Dunbarella* (fig. 5, p. 151) and *Pteronites*. *Posidonia* (bivalve) and *Bollandites* (ammonoid) have also been recorded at this locality. This is a good example of a faunal marker horizon as the bed can be traced to other parts of the Bowland Sub-Basin. Return to the car by retracing your steps along Bonstone Brook.

Fig. 4 Gravity slide in the Hodder Mudstone Formation, Bonstone Brook near Newton. Paul Kabrna is pointing out the area of downslope movement. Photo © David Nelson (CPGS).

Fig. 5 The bivalve *Dunbarella* sp. was collected in Paper Mill Wood [SD 6803 4338] from the Dunbarella Bed which lies within the Chaigley Limestone. If you look closely there is a bryozoa encrusted to the umbo (Inset). The scale is in mm. Photo © Nick Riley, British Geological Survey, Keyworth, Nottingham.

Limestone Knolls of the Cow Ark Anticline, Throstle Nest Anticline, and Whitewell Anticline

Purpose
The broad aim of this excursion is to investigate the limestone knolls at Hall Hill, Bowland with Leagram, and Long Knots.

Background
The dramatic limestone knoll landscapes seen during the course of this excursion have continually attracted visitors for many years. Some consider the area might have been the inspiration for J. R. R. Tolkien's Shire i.e., the home to the hobbits. Regrettably localities on this excursion require the continued use of a car. Parking at localities 2 and 5 needs careful planning. Refreshments and toilet facilities are available at the 14th century Inn at Whitewell, a very busy pub especially at weekends. The Inn forms part of the Duchy of Lancaster Estate.

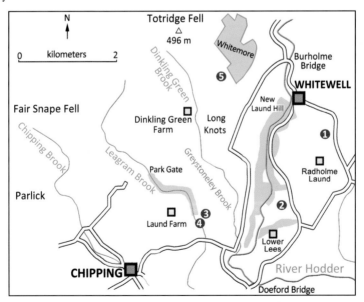

Fig. 1   Sketch map of the area between Whitewell and Chipping showing the localities and roads for the excursion.

Locality 1   Coplow Limestone, Hall Hill Quarry [SD 667 466]

From the Inn at Whitewell proceed in an easterly direction up the relatively steep Hall Hill Road for just over 1 km to a lay-by on the left. Hall Hill Quarry is in the field to the right and can be reached by a public footpath. Even though the quarry is adjacent to the footpath, permission to visit the locality is required from Radholme Laund Farm, Cow Ark, BB7 3DF. There are spectacular views from the top of the quarry towards Dunsop Bridge to the north, and the Vale of Chipping to the southwest. There are also excellent views of limestone knolls across the Hodder river to the west.

Fig. 2   Crinoidal Coplow Limestone from Hall Hill Quarry. The disarticulated parts of many crinoids have been well preserved. The arrow points to a 2 cm wide *Gilbertsocrinus* crinoid calyx.

Hall Hill Quarry (fig. 17, p. 26) is exposed on the northern limb of the Cow Ark Anticline and has been extensively quarried along the south face which runs east-west for about 70 m. The first part of the outcrop is by the limekiln which has been excavated into solid rock. There are 4 m of bioclastic flank and inter-bank facies dipping 25° to the north. The limestone comprises pale grey, wavy-bedded, medium- to coarse-grained siliceous crinoidal packstones. Calyces of common crinoids found at Hall Hill Quarry include *Actinocrinites* and *Gilbertsocrinus*. The trilobite *Phillipsia gemmulifera* has been recovered confirming Coplow Limestone age. Incidentally the poor condition of the wall at the top of the knoll I suspect is partly the result of many years of fossil collecting!

In the main part of the quarry these facies by the lime kiln pass up into the core of a Waulsortian mud-mound of poorly bedded micritic wackestones. Below the mud-mound, flank and inter-bank limestones extend from east to west. Dolosilt (fig.18, p.27) is easily recognised as a thin tough veneer of brown silty limestone which appears to have been plastered onto the surfaces of limestone beds.

Locality 2   Limekiln Wood Limestone, Ing Wood [SD 656 448]
Return to the car and proceed to the Inn at Whitewell. Turn left on to Whitewell Road for 2 km to Ing Wood. On your way to locality 2 the Chatburn Limestone is exposed in the core of the Whitewell Anticline to your left. At Ing Wood park near the stile on the grass verge. Additional parking for more cars may be possible 100 m before you reach Ing Wood on the right-hand side of the road, providing you seek permission from the land owner. Cross the stile and after walking 350 m southwest there is a disused quarry with a lime kiln. Permission to visit this locality must be sought from Lower Lees Farm, Cow Ark, BB7 3DQ.

Fig.3   Limekiln Wood Limestone boulder bed southwest of Ing Wood. The hammer for scale (see arrow) rests on top of the dark grey Waulsortian limestone.

The quarry lies on the southern limb of the Whitewell Anticline and exposes Limekiln Wood Limestone (fig.3) at the base of the Hodder Mudstone Formation. This limestone is well developed over the eroded Waulsortian limestone of the underlying Clitheroe Limestone Formation. The outcrop consists of detrital crinoidal limestone seen here as a spectacular limestone breccia and boulder bed embedded in crinoidal mudstone; some of the boulders are over 2 m across.

Locality 3   Coplow Limestone, Knot Hill [SD 639 447]

Return to the car and continue south along Whitewell Road to Doeford Bridge. Cross the bridge and after 185 m turn right into Little Bowland Road. At the next road junction bear left for another 450 m to the entrance for Leagram Brook and Knot Hill. Permission to continue to locality 3 and 4 should be obtained from Laund Farm, Bowland with Leagram, Chipping, PR3 2QS Tel: 01995 61348 (www.sheepmilkuk.co.uk). It may be possible to drive up the farm track for another 880 m to Knot Barn where parking is possible off the farm track by the old lime kiln.

Knot Hill is a disused quarry which exposes Coplow Limestone in the western core of the Throstle Nest Anticline. There are numerous faces to examine, some of which are up to 8 m high. These massive Waulsortian limestone comprises wackestones with sheet-spars. In the north-western corner of the quarry, flank facies of medium- to coarse-grained crinoidal packstones and grainstones overlie a Waulsortian mud-mound. Fossils recorded from here include the trilobites *Bollandia* sp., *Weania* sp., and the diagnostic *Phillipsia gemmulifera* which confirms Coplow Limestone age.

Locality 4   Leagram Mudstone, Leagram Brook [SD 639 447]

From Knot Hill cross the field in a westerly direction along the path marked on the O.S. map towards Leagram Brook. Descend towards the footbridge and turn south following the brook to a shale cliff meander. The distance from locality 3 to the outcrop at the shale cliff meander is about 600 m.

The Leagram Mudstone (fig.26, p.34) is exposed in a 5 m high meander cliff in the core of the Throstle Nest Anticline about 20 m above the Waulsortian limestones seen at the previous locality. The outcrop comprises blocky, calcareous, dark mudstones, and muddy wackestones. The ammonoid *Merocanites* has been found here. Return to the car.

Locality 5   Bellman Limestone, Long Knots [SD 645 466]

Return along Little Bowland Road (fig. 4) and at the first junction turn left along the same road for a further 3.8 km. Park carefully along the roadside across from a small disused Bellman Limestone quarry to the east. Take the stile and footpath by the car across to a limestone outcrop on the farm track up towards Tunstall Ing. Continue along the road for 400 m and then take a grassy path northeast towards Lower Fence Wood for 170 m to the Calamine Mine. Permission to visit this locality should be obtained from New Laund Farm, Little Bowland Road, Whitewell, BB7 3BN.

Ascend to the top of the hill above the Calamine Mine adit for excellent views of the surrounding countryside. The prominent series of steep-sided hills may have inspired the early geologists to introduce the term 'knoll'. The limestones in the vicinity of the adit are slightly dolomitised, a process which resulted in differential weathering of echinoderm fossils. Very well preserved blastoids belonging to *Ellipticoblastus ellipticus* have been found here. Thin veins of sphalerite (zinc blend) and smithsonite (calamine) were formerly worked in the adit. Return to the car.

Fig. 4   En route from Leagram Brook to the Calamine Mine at Dinkling Green, the landscape becomes dominated by a series of limestone knolls. This photograph is taken at the southern end of Long Knots. These knolls are composed of Bellman Limestone, Clitheroe Limestone Formation.

Pendle Hill and Clitheroe

Purpose
The aim of this excursion is to examine the Pendle Grit Formation on Pendle Hill, and the Waulsortian limestones and fossils of Salthill Quarry.

Background
The main Pendle Grit quarry is located in Wiswell (pronounced wizell), a small village near Whalley. Wiswell is said to have taken its name from Old Molly's Well, later known as the wise woman's well. The first record of Wiswell is in a charter of 1193, in the reign of Richard the Lionheart. Salthill Quarry Geology Trail straddles the Forest of Bowland and the Pendle Hill AONB. Clitheroe's Norman Keep is at least 800 years old and sits on top of a limestone knoll. The recently renovated Clitheroe Castle Museum provides all the modern amenities, with good views over the Ribble Valley, Pendle Hill and the Vale of Chipping.

Morning
The Pendle Grit quarries at Wiswell are best approached from the village of Sabden. Drive along Whalley Road for 4.5 km and then take a right turn marked Cul-de-sac into Clerk Hill Road. Continue along this single track road for a further 2 km to Wiswell Moor Houses. The final 300 m is along a farm track. The land-owner at Wiswell Moor Houses encourages visitors to the quarry as long as they do not obstruct access. I recommend you consult Chapter 4 by Ian Kane on the Pendle Grit before you start the excursion.

Locality 1   Wiswell Moor Quarry [SD 754 371]
Pass through the farm gate at Wiswell Moor Houses and follow the track for 500 m to another farm gate next to the Wireless Station. Take the path which runs down the grassy slope and use the stiles to get to the quarry which is designated Open Access Land. As you approach the top quarry there are good views of Whalley Nab to the southeast and Clitheroe to the north. There is a lot of fairly complex sedimentology here so consult chapter 4 by Ian Kane on the Pendle Grit prior to visiting this site. Boots and hard hat are advisable when navigating in and out of the 3 quarries.

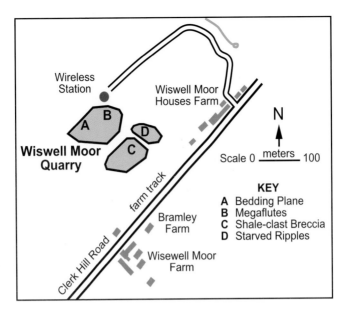

Fig. 1 Sketch map of Wiswell Moor Quarry showing the route to the quarry from Wiswell Moor Houses to the Wireless Station. The approximate position of some of the main features of the quarry marked **A, B C,** and **D** are identified in the key.

There are approximately 80 m of strata exposed stratigraphically through the Pendle Grit Formation sandstones and siltstones in Wiswell Quarry. Here you can see excellent undulose bedding plane exposures (**A**), observe the various facies, and walk through the stratigraphy (due to the relatively steep structural dip here). The outcrops consist of thickly-bedded, massive, medium- to coarse-grained arkosic sandstone beds. Scours or flutes are common at the bases of beds (fig 2), and occasionally scoured surfaces are laterally persistent. Good examples of scours are exposed in cross-section in the top quarry below the Wireless Station (**B**). Individual beds are commonly covered by shale-clast rich tops (**C**) which commonly define amalgamation surfaces (fig.3). Towards the top of the sequence beds tend to thin and siltstone beds become more frequent. At the very top of the sequence there are very well preserved starved ripples (**D**).

Return to the car and take the same route back to Sabden. Turn left along Clitheroe Road and after 1.5 km park in the lay-by at the top of the Nick of Pendle. For those intrigued by the name, the 'Nick' is an overflow channel formed by the action of glacial meltwater during the last ice age.

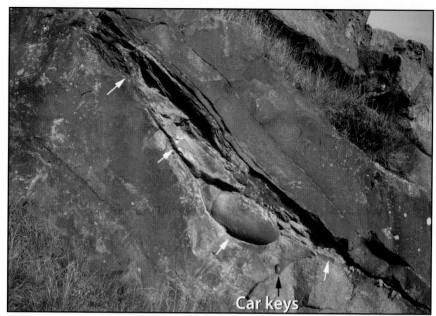

Fig. 2   The white arrows mark the base of a scour or flute as seen in the top quarry near position **B** on the sketch map. Note the large concretion resting in the bottom of the scour. Car keys for scale..

Fig. 3   This is a shale-clast breccia which is believed to have been formed from a debris flow. The abundant shale clasts are often deformed and there are some large coalified plant fragments. This locality is near position **C** on the sketch map. Jeff Peakall of Leeds University is inspecting the outcrop.

Locality 2   Nick of Pendle Quarries [SD 772 386]
Besides being the type locality for the Pendle Grit Formation, the Nick of Pendle is also a good vantage point to view the regional geology from the top of the hill above the car park (weather permitting). There are excellent panoramic views towards the northern margin of the Bowland Sub-Basin and across to Waddington Fell overlying the Bowland intrabasinal high. To the south, prominent topographic ridges and valleys are formed by overlying Kinderscoutian and Marsdenian progradational systems in the area of the Burnley Coalfield. There are also excellent views of the line of limestone knolls, from the topographically dominant Worsaw Hill, to the Castle in the centre of Clitheroe.

The small northernmost quarry across from the car park has a good example of a loaded bed base; these bulbous loading structures indicate that the underlying mudstone was soft when the turbidite bed above was deposited. The other quarry sections have similar features to those already seen at Wiswell Quarry e.g., scours, amalgamated beds, and ripples.

Afternoon
From the car park at the Nick of Pendle continue towards Clitheroe for 3 km until you reach the main A59 road. Turn right for 1.8 km and then left onto Pimlico Link Road signposted Chatburn/Waddington. After a further 800 m turn left into Lincoln Way for Salthill Quarry. The car park is a further 300 m on the right-hand side of the road.

Locality 1   Waulsortian Mud-Mound [SD 755 426]
Salthill Quarry is an SSSI and is currently owned by Ribble Valley Borough Council and managed by the Lancashire Wildlife Trust. The first geology trail at Salthill was devised by Robin Grayson in 1981 and published by the Nature Conservancy Council. An updated version of the trail by Bowden et al. 1997 was jointly published by the Lancashire Wildlife Trust and the Geologists' Association. The trail is a circular walk of about 1.5 km and the localities visited on this excursion broadly follow those of the updated trail.

The trail begins by the information board in front of the limestone outcrop at the car park. This quarry face exposes a cross-section through a mud-mound. If you have difficulty working out where the core of the mound is in relation to the overlying beds of limestone, look at the photograph in Chapter 2

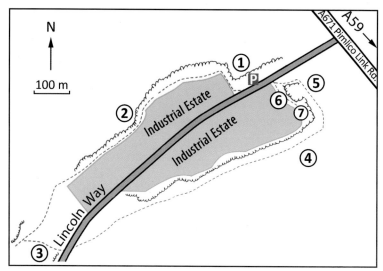

Fig. 4 Sketch map of Salthill Quarry showing the main localities and the parking place. Those connected with the industrial estate may also be making use of the car park, however, there are spaces reserved for visitors to the geology trail.

(fig. 14, p. 23) of this face taken after a prolonged period of heavy rain. The dome at the centre of the face is composed of light grey unbedded micritic mud that corresponds to the bank facies of Miller & Grayson (1972). The darker more muddy thinly-bedded limestone that drapes across the core of the mud-mound is the crinoidal-rich inter-bank facies. These muddier beds represent a calmer environment in which fossils, especially crinoids, suffered minor disarticulation, and are therefore generally well preserved.

By following the path around the corner the outcrop confirms the fact that this is indeed a three-dimensional structure and not just a weathered surface! Other features to look out for are boulder beds which were formed during erosion of the mud-mound. The Salthill Quarry Geology Trail guide also depicts the Tournaisian - Viséan unconformity at the top of the pale grey mud-mound. The sharp undulatory nature of the top of the mound may be a feature of its formation or indeed a product of erosion.

Locality 2   Flank limestone [SD 753 426]
Continue along the path for 200 m and stop at the marker post and approach the quarry face through the trees. The limestone outcrop is composed of flank limestone. Compared to the inter-bank limestone, flank limestone

(fig. 5) is well-bedded, paler grey, still richly crinoidal, but nowhere near as muddy. The disarticulated crinoid parts suggest some sorting in currents in a slightly higher energy regime. Geopetal infillings within clusters of crinoid stems indicate depositional slopes from 2° to 22° at this locality.

Fig. 5   The search for geopetal infills in the flank limestone at locality 2. The inset (scale: 20 cm wide) illustrates just how crinoidal-rich these limestones are.

Locality 3   Flank limestone [SD 752 424]

Follow the path for 300 m and keep left at the junction for another 100 m until you come to some steps that lead down to Lincoln Way. Locality 3 is at the bottom of the steps on your right.

Although this is another outcrop of flank limestone, the fossils here are more varied and more abundant than the previous locality. On the bedding planes there are well preserved crinoid calyces, corals and brachiopods. It is also much easier to see the dip of the beds; in this case they are dipping about 25° South. The orientation of the crinoid stems suggests that they are roughly aligned by the action of steady currents.

Locality 4   Salthill Cap Beds [SD 756 425]

Cross the road and climb up the steps. Follow the path for 500 m until you reach a grassy slope on your right. The recently constructed 'crinoid bench' is composed of Bellman Limestone. The three carved panels are intended to illustrate the anatomical details of the crinoid form.

The Salthill Cap Beds are grainstones (biosparites). They contain very little mud content being mainly composed of the remains of crinoids (fig.6). The lack of mud is probably a consequence of the grainstones being deposited on a palaeoslope. The mud content was probably winnowed out by the action of currents. At the bottom of the outcrop the grainstones become more muddy indicating proximity to the succeeding Leagram Mudstone concealed beneath the vegetation. The number of well-preserved crinoid calyces collected from this locality have contributed to making Salthill Quarry an internationally important site. The fossil plates in chapter 3 of Donovan & Lewis will help you to identify crinoid calyces that you might see at this site.

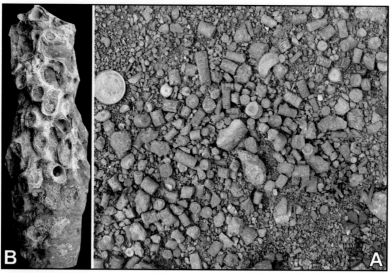

Fig.6   **A** The limestone at locality 4 is mainly composed of disarticulated parts of crinoids. Two pence for scale.   **B** Crinoid stems can sometimes be found with parasites attached. This single crinoid stem has the tabulate coral *Cladochonus* wrapped around it. Scale: Stem is 1 cm wide.

- 163 -

Locality 5   Viewpoint [SD 756 425]

Follow the path for 50 m to the ridge that separates units in the industrial complex and stop by the information board for good views of the Ribble Valley. Waddington Fell lies to the northwest with Pendle Hill to the southeast. Looking east-northeast you can see the continuation of the limestone knolls in Warren Hill and Worsaw Hill. Turn around and look towards Clitheroe town centre, and with luck, you might just make out the limestone knoll on which Clitheroe Castle stands.

Locality 6   Inter-bank and Flank limestones [SD 7564 4262]

Continue along the path on the ridge towards the car park. Follow the fence to the bottom of the incline and turn left for the next locality.

The key feature here is the rapid lateral facies change which has been illustrated on Figure 5, page 23. If you look closely at the outcrop, you may be able to see mud-mound bank beds at the base and top of the sequence.

Locality 7   Waulsortian Mud-Mound [SD 7566 4259]

The central part of the face is part of a large Waulsortian mud-mound. The Salthill Quarry Trail guide describes an unconformity towards the top of the sequence, although it is not easy to recognise. Above the unconformity there are abundant fossils preserved in wavy-bedded limestone formed from the rapid growth of a calcareous sponge. Other fossils noted include the tabulate coral *Syringopora* and the rugose coral *Lithostrotion*.

At locality 7 a fence prevents access to the south face of the quarry where there are a series of boulder beds, mainly composed of bank limestone, set in a calcareous mudstone matrix. Miller and Grayson recorded geopetals from several of the boulders confirming that some of the boulders are upside-down in relation to their original bed position. The boulder beds are believed to have formed in gullies, and the overlying grainstones (biosparites) of locality 4 filled in the spaces thus smoothing out the sea-floor topography.

Optional locality   Clitheroe Castle Keep [SD 742 416]

Leave Salthill Quarry and make your way to the centre of town and park in a public car park, most of which are pay and display. Proceed to Clitheroe Castle for the museum, refreshments, and the mud-mound as shown in Figure 7 on page 165. This is always a good option in inclement weather.

Fig. 7 Clitheroe Castle was built by Robert de Lacy around 1186 and is one of the smallest motte and bailey castles in the country. It has been built on top of a limestone knoll, (Bellman Limestone Member, Clitheroe Limestone Formation). Fossils have been made more conspicuous following cleaning of the mound. To the right of the steps leading up to the Keep there is a well-preserved fissure in the limestone knoll.

Lothersdale Anticline and Cowling

Purpose
The aim of this excursion is to examine the succession from the Mid-Viséan limestones and mudstones of Raygill Quarry, Lothersdale, to the Namurian Sabden Shales in Stonehead Beck, Cowling.

Background
Lothersdale is a village and civil parish in the Craven district of North Yorkshire. It is a small community of about 200 houses and the Pennine Way runs through it. Raygill Fishing Lakes offers year-round trout and coarse fishing, a cafe, and a Wildlife and History Trail for young children. The fishing lakes have been established in a disused quarry which is the first locality of this excursion. Raygill Fisheries web site states: 'Lothersdale is in a forgotten valley. Sat Navs are obsolete in this area and will send you down tracks that have not been roads for 30 years'.

Raygill quarry was made famous in the late nineteenth century through the discovery by Tiddeman of a cache of bones from the last Interglacial. The report of the Raygill Fissure Exploration Committee stated: '*The fissure occurs in an anticlinal of limestone in Lothersdale, near Skipton. The limestone is extensively quarried, and whilst removing the limestone, the fissure, which descends almost perpendicularly, has repeatedly exhibited new sections during several years past. It was decided by the Yorkshire Geological and Polytechnic Society to investigate its contents in 1879, and a grant was made by the British Association to assist in this object. It was found that the fissure contained, besides laminated clay and layers of sand and stones, a brown sandy clay with rounded boulders of sandstone and limestone derived from the immediate locality, and numerous bones of animals. The latter comprise the bones, teeth, and tusks of elephant, teeth of rhinoceros, hippopotamus, hyaena, bear, and others, broken horns of the roebuck, and bones of birds. The bones are, when found, soft and friable; and, being cemented to the matrix, are frequently difficult to extricate and individualise. The Committee express their indebtedness to Mr. Spencer, the proprietor of the quarry, and to Mr. Todd, for the kind manner in which they have assisted in the operations.* (Source: Nature, 4th October, 1883)

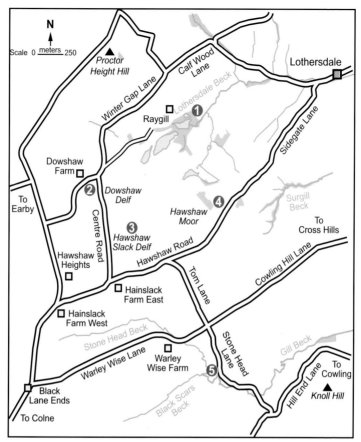

Fig. 1 Sketch map of the Lothersdale area showing the approximate positions of the localities. Lothersdale is 8 km from Colne and Skipton. There are brown tourist signs 5 km away in each direction to aid navigation to Raygill Fisheries.

Locality 1   Embsay Limestone, Raygill Quarry [SD 943 455]

For arranging a visit and car parking at Raygill Quarry, you should contact the owner / manager of Raygill Fisheries based in the new fishery lodge. Tel: 01535 632500 / 631428.

From the fishing lodge take the path to the left and continue along the lakeside for about 150 m. The Embsay Limestone (fig. 2) is a pale coloured packstone which comprises fine detrital carbonate that was derived from the Askrigg shelf and gravitationally fed into the Bowland Sub-Basin. The base is not seen but at the southwest corner of the quarry, the limestone passes conformably into Hodder Mudstones ('Skibeden Shales with limestones' of Hudson and Mitchell, 1937). After 150 m there is a barytes vein which crosses the quarry in an east-west direction.

Return to the fishing lodge and take the other path around the outskirts of the quarry for 350 m until you reach an isolated hut. The last 30 m involves careful descent to the lake where the same barytes vein outcrops (fig. 27, p. 35). By the shore some of the limestone is bioturbated, however, the proximity to the lake makes this locality hazardous. Bray (1927) confirmed that fossils in the limestone are quite rare, however, the quarry manager of the time did report finding a selection of brachiopods, a gastropod, but no corals.

Ascend to the path and continue for a further 230 m to where the core of the Lothersdale Anticline is exposed. As you approach the outcrop it is readily identifiable by the steeply folded beds. In the southwest corner the overlying Hodder Mudstones are clearly seen but definitely not accessible. From here return to the car and proceed to the next locality.

Fig. 2 The main Raygill lake with Embsay Limestone outcropping on both sides. The arrow points to the site where the photograph for Figure 27 page 35 was taken. The fissures that revealed the cache of bones during the late nineteenth century were located on the quarry face in shadow.

Locality 2   Twiston Sandstone, Dowshaw Delf [SD 935 448]

Return to the main road through Lothersdale village. At the junction turn left for 2.25 km up Calf Wood Lane which runs into Winter Gap Lane. Permission to visit and park at Dowshaw Delf Quarry should be sought from Dowshaw Farm, Lothersdale, Keighley BD20 8HN directly opposite the quarry.

Dowshaw Delf is a disused Embsay Limestone quarry composed of predominantly thin- to thick-bedded packstones and grainstones. Some of the beds contain lenses of chert and thin subordinate mudstones. The overlying Twiston Sandstone is located in the far southeast corner of the delf [SD 9350 4482]. It is a thin- to thick-bedded medium grained, calcareous and siliceous sandstone. The lithostratigraphic succession (fig.3, p.11) shows the base of the Twiston Sandstone as one of the basins local unconformities. In Dowshaw Delf the sandstone can be seen resting with angular unconformity on Embsay Limestone. This also represents one of the earliest inputs of terrestrial sand into the basin. Return to the car.

Locality 3   Pendleside Limestone, Hawshaw Slack Delf [SD 940 445]

From Dowshaw Delf retrace your steps along the road for 180 m and turn right up Centre Road for just under 1 km. Turn left along Hawshaw Road for 500 m and stop at the farm gate prior to where the road diverges. Permission to enter the delf should be arranged with the land-owner at Hawshaw Heights, Lothersdale, Keighley BB20 8HP. Follow the farm track for about 230 m northwest down the slope until you arrive at Hawshaw Slack Delf. On your right-hand side there is a local car racetrack!

The Pendleside Limestone exposed in the delf dips steeply to the south. It comprises thin- to thick-bedded limestones with a few irregular bands of black chert. The very thin-bedded units seem to be calcareous siltstones. Small-scale flexuring of the beds is a common feature in the quarry. The best example of slumping in Hawshaw Slack Delf is shown on Figure 31 page 40. Fossils are scarce in the limestone being restricted to crinoid debris. By contrast, in the Bowland Shales which overlie the Pendleside Limestone in the quarry, Bray (1927) recorded the bivalve *Posidonia becheri* and the ammonoid *Arnsbergites sphaericostriatus* (formerly *Goniatites sphaericostriatus*). Return to the car and proceed to the next locality on foot as parking further along Hawshaw Road is not advisable.

Fig. 3 Higher up at the northern end of Hawshaw Slack Delf the Pendleside Limestone exhibits dramatic folding. Steve Birch of Craven & Pendle Geological Society is studying the outcrop.

Locality 4   Pendle Grit, Hawshaw Moor [SD 947 446]

Permission to visit this site should be sought from New Lane Head Farm, Lothersdale, BD20 8HT. Tel: 01535 637911. From the farm gate at locality 3 proceed on foot for 775 m along Hawshaw Road until you reach farm buildings on your left. The locality is in the field to the right of the farm buildings about 100 m to the northwest in a shallow disused quarry.

The outcrop of Pendle Grit is typically a coarse-grained feldspathic sandstone which trends northeast to southwest linking Town Edge, Hawshaw Moor and Kelbrook Moor. There are a series of dip faults with westerly downthrows that effectively offset the outcrop. Although the exposure is small compared to Wiswell Moor and Waddington Fell Quarry, the outcrop does show sandstone units pinching out into a well developed intraformational shale-clast conglomerate. The shale clasts, which are deformed and elongated, were eroded by turbidite flows which deposited the Pendle Grit.

Locality 5   Stonehead Beck [SD 946 437]

Return to the car at locality 3. Follow the road and keep to the right along Tom Lane. Stay on this road for 700 m until you arrive at a cross-roads. Parking is possible on the grassy roadside of Cowling Hill Lane. If you follow Cowling Hill Lane down hill in a westerly direction for 275 m there is limited parking by Warley Wise Bridge. The farm towards the centre of the photograph (fig. 4 A) is Warley Wise Farm from which the Warley Wise Grit derived its name. On foot make you way from the cross-roads down Stonehead Lane for 500 m until you arrive at Stonehead Farm. Permission to enter Stonehead Beck must be sought from the land-owner.

In 1984 a proposal was put forward by the Subcommission on Carboniferous Stratigraphy to establish a formal boundary between the upper and lower parts of the Carboniferous System. In 1985 a list of potential worldwide sites to investigate were drawn up with Stonehead Beck being proposed as the potential Mid-Carboniferous stratotype for Europe. Geologists working on the ammonoid assemblage and microfossils concluded that Stonehead Beck represents the most complete sequence across the Mid-Carboniferous boundary interval (Riley et al., 1987) confirming that it is the best site for a European stratotype. Generally, there is a gap at this boundary, and most other sections are incomplete, due to a major sea-level fall that was probably caused by the growth of a major ice sheet over the South Pole.

Stonehead Beck is an SSSI. It is located at the north-western end of the Pendle Monocline. The strata exposed consists of hemipelagic mudstones of the Namurian Sabden Shales (fig. 3, p. 11). These shales were deposited in a low energy offshore environment that was subjected to periods of fluctuating salinity. During periods of high salinity, fully marine conditions are marked by marine bands containing a diagnostic ammonoid fauna. By contrast, barren silty intervals are usually sparsely fossiliferous and indicate periods of low salinity levels. Such stressful environmental conditions are generally associated with low diversity, high abundance faunas. Fossil bands are less than 2 m thick and include ammonoids, bivalves, fish debris and bits of plant material. The shales also contain nodular wackestone bands. Early lithification of these wackestone nodules is associated with the preservation of uncrushed fossils, whereas in the softer shales, fossils are generally more fragile and often compressed.

Many major ammonoid lineages disappeared at the Mid-Carboniferous boundary and there is little doubt that, for this group at least, the interval was a major crisis. Incidentally this is the only excursion locality where Mississippian and Pennsylvanian age strata are exposed in the same section.

Fig. 4   A   Namurian Sabden Shales exposed in the bank of Stonehead Beck, Cowling, North Yorkshire.   B   Ferruginous wackestone nodules encased in black fissile Sabden Shales.   C   Silty shales showing a variety of small fossils including bivalves and ammonoids. Hammer for scale.

Eshton-Hetton Anticline and the Skipton Anticline

Purpose
The broad aim of this excursion is to explore key Viséan SSSI localities and the Skipton Rock Fault in the northeast corner of the Bowland Sub-Basin.

Background
This excursion lies within North Yorkshire, with some of the localities falling within the Yorkshire Dales National Park. The main town Skipton is known as the 'Gateway to the Dales' even though it is just outside the Yorkshire Dales National Park. To the north of the excursion area lies the southern margin of the Askrigg Block. This topographically elevated region is separated from the Bowland Sub-Basin by the Craven Fault System. Shallow water limestones deposited on the Askrigg Block are in marked contrast to the basinal carbonate turbidites and mudstones of this excursion.

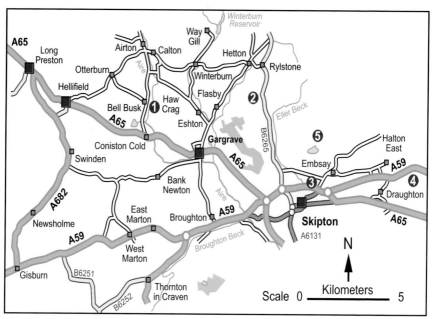

Fig. 1   Sketch map showing the approximate position of the localities around Skipton and Gargrave, North Yorkshire.

Locality 1   Haw Crag Quarry, Bell Busk [SD 914 564]

From Gargrave follow the A65 west for 3 km and turn right for Bell Busk. Continue along the narrow road for about 1.5 km north (under a railway bridge); turn sharp right at the first turning and park on the grass verge by a small bridge over the River Aire [SD 905 564]. It is a 20 minute walk via Crag Laithe to Haw Crag Quarry (fig. 2) which includes 1 km by rough farm track with slight ascent.

The key feature of this quarry, which is situated on the Eshton-Hetton Anticline, is the sharp irregular unconformable junction between Thornton Limestone and the overlying Hodder Mudstones. The strata immediately overlying the Thornton Limestone is 2 m of limestone conglomerate known as the Haw Crag Boulder Bed [SD 9142 5637], an SSSI since 1954. Note the huge upturned blocks of bedded wackestone (Hetton Beck Limestone) within the boulder deposit. The limestone conglomerate thickens to about 20 m when traced northwards in the quarry. Fossils are generally abundant and include corals, brachiopods and crinoids.

Fig. 2   Haw Crag Boulder Bed, Bell Busk, North Yorkshire. The arrows indicate the inclined junction of the unconformity. Thornton Limestone lies below the arrows and Hodder Mudstone above. The O.S. map indicates the scale.

Locality 2   Clints Rock Quarry, Rylstone [SD 967 575]

It is possible to drive to Rylstone via Airton, Winterburn and Hetton by very narrow lanes but a much easier route is to return to the A65 and turn left to

Skipton. Turn left at a roundabout after 8 km signed for Grassington and left at the next roundabout onto the B6265 for a further 6.5 km to Rylstone. Park at a large lay-by on the left hand side immediately past the village. Leave your car and follow the road back to the pond at Rylstone. Turn right and then left along Back Lane which leads into Green Lane. Take the footpath southwest towards the railway line. Turn south-southeast after High Croft Plantation and proceed to Clints Rock Quarry. The main quarry face is in a hollow to the right. Total walking distance from the lay-by to the quarry is just under 2 km. Permission to visit the quarry should be sought from Flasby Hall Farm, Flasby, Skipton, North Yorkshire BD23 3PX.

Clints Rock Quarry [SE 9669 5751] is situated on the south-eastern flank of the Eshton-Hetton Anticline. It has been an SSSI since 1955 for its various limestone lithologies which includes 'Tiddeman's Breccia', a Pendleside Limestone conglomerate. A key feature is the unconformity between well-bedded crinoidal Pendleside Limestone and the calcareous muddy limestones of the Hodder Mudstone Formation. Figure 3 shows that there is no angular discordance visible. This unconformity at the base of the Pendleside Limestone also occurs in Hambleton Quarry (locality 4) on the Skipton Anticline. Clints Rock Quarry is also considered to be one of the richest zaphrentoid coral localities in England. The fossil zaphrentoid coral, *Rylstonia*, was named after the quarry in 1927. Return to the car and proceed to locality 3 in Skipton.

Fig. 3 Clints Rock Quarry, Rylstone, North Yorkshire. The arrows indicate the inclined surface of the unconformity between the Pendleside Limestone at the top and the Hodder Mudstones below. The scale is indicated on the photograph.

Locality 3   Skipton Rock Quarry, Skipton [SE 010 530]

Drive to Skipton along the B6265. After 6.5 km turn left at the roundabout and then proceed along the A59 for 2 km. The entrance to Skipton Rock Quarry is on your left. The locality is 500 m along the quarry road (with speed ramps) on the right. Permission to enter quarry should be sought from Skipton Rock Quarry, Harrogate Road, Skipton, BD23 6AB Tel: 01756 702026 Email: quarry.skipton@tarmac.co.uk. Boots, hard hat, and high visibility vest are essential.

Skipton Rock Quarry is situated in the core of the east-northeast trending Skipton Anticline which runs from Skipton to Bolton Abbey. The anticline, which forms part of the Ribblesdale Fold Belt, is symmetrical with fairly steep dips on the northern limb. The main feature at this locality is the striking deformation caused by the Skipton Rock Fault (fig. 4), a reverse fault developed near the axis of the anticline. The limestone that used to be quarried here is the steeply dipping bioturbated Haw Bank Limestone, which is equivalent to the Chatburn Limestone in the Ribble Valley.

Fig. 4   A reverse fault (arrowed) is developed near the axis of the Skipton Anticline in Skipton Rock Quarry. Features like this are thought to be caused by a period of strike-slip (or wrench) fault movement after the compression that produced the anticline. Such structures are related to deformation associated with the South Craven Fault system which occurs immediately to the south of this location.

Locality 4   Hambleton Quarry, Skipton [SE 058 534]

Hambleton Quarry is 6 km east along the A59 shortly before Bolton Abbey Railway Station on your right. Proceed along the A59 for 5 km and park in the long lay-by on the left [SE 049 533]. This is 1 km before the quarry and using as few cars as possible drive to the quarry entrance. The track to the quarry is immediately after Hambleton Garage. There is space for no more than 4 or 5 cars in front of the gate at the entrance to the quarry. Permission to enter the quarry is required from the Chatsworth Settlement Trustees, Estate Office, Bolton Abbey, Skipton, North Yorkshire BD23 6EX. Boots, hard hat, and high visibility vest are essential.

Hambleton Quarry (figs. 5, 6, 7) is located on the southeast flank of the Skipton Anticline, and has been an SSSI since 1991. The minor fold structure is the most visually striking feature seen as you enter the quarry. The lowermost unit is the Hodder Mudstone Formation seen as discontinuous exposures at the eastern end of the quarry. The section comprises less than 10 m of thick dolomitic mudstone with subordinate silty limestone beds.

The Pendleside Limestone is best seen towards the southwest end of the quarry where it appears as a thick succession of well-bedded turbiditic and conglomeratic limestone beds with minor shale interbeds. Within this sequence there is a distinctive 2 m thick limestone breccia bed consisting of angular to subrounded clasts of bioclastic limestone up to 30 cm diameter. This breccia bed is well displayed in the hollow beneath the core of the fold. The unit is the widely recognised marker bed commonly referred to as Tiddeman's Breccia. Overlying the breccia bed are darker, thinner-bedded, sandy-coloured limestones, with thin shale interbeds. A change in colour to grey-black at the very top marks the arrival of Bowland Shale deposited as hemipelagic sediments below storm wave base, with some carbonate turbidites introduced through storm activity on the Cracoean reefs.

The overturned bedding plane of Pendleside Limestone on the northwest face of the quarry is covered with load structures, a feature caused by soft-sediment deformation. These bulbous features indicate that the underlying bed was soft when the turbidite bed above was deposited. Trace fossils are also present on the bedding planes.

Return to the car, and if there is time, an optional locality you may like to consider is Witshaw Bank Quarry at Embsay Reservoir.

Fig. 5 Asymmetric fold in Hambleton Quarry, North Yorkshire. **B** marks the position of the fold and the Pendleside Limestone breccia (fig. 6 below). **C** marks the position of the load structures (fig. 7 below).

Fig. 6 The Pendleside Limestone in the core of the fold is composed of a variety of angular and sub-rounded clasts which were deposited by a turbidite debris flow.

Fig. 7 Loaded bed base on the northwest face of the quarry. The inset photograph is a close up of the rock face as indicated by the arrow. Hammer for scale.

Locality 5   Witshaw Bank Quarry, Skipton [SE 058 535]

Take the Skipton road along the A59. After about 3 km turn right into Holme Lane for Embsay. Continue for 2.8 km into Embsay village. Stay on this road until you reach the Elm Tree Inn. Bear right into Pasture Road which leads to Embsay Reservoir. As you approach the reservoir there is a sign for the public car park with speed ramps on the final approach. From the car park Witshaw Bank Quarry can be seen on the opposite side of the reservoir. Follow the footpath on the western side of the reservoir for about 1.2 km until you reach the quarry.

In this small abandoned Pendle Grit quarry (fig. 8) above Embsay reservoir there are 30 m of coarse-grained, thickly bedded sandstones exposed at the base of a channel complex. The site also offers good views over the Skipton Anticline. Clean surfaces reveal complex internal amalgamation surfaces. Beds appear channelised and there is a significant development of shale-clast horizons both at the bases and tops of beds.

Fig. 8   Witshaw Bank Quarry at Embsay Reservoir. Between sandstone beds there are some laterally impersistent chaotic shale-clast conglomerates. Sheep for scale.

Acknowledgements

I would like to thank Dr. Nick Riley MBE (British Geological Survey, Keyworth), Professor Paul Wignall (University of Leeds), Ian Kane (Statoil ASA, Bergen, Norway), Dr. Colin Waters (British Geological Survey, Keyworth), Jeremy J. Savill (CPGS), David Turner (CPGS), and David Nelson (CPGS) for taking the time to review, comment or contribute photographs for the excursions. A special thanks is extended to the Duchy of Lancaster for their support through the Duchy of Lancaster Benevolent Fund. The support of the Hoseasons Group is also greatly appreciated. Last but not least, my thanks to the land owners and tenant farmers who have allowed access to localities described in the excursions.

References

Bowden, A., Webster, M. & Mitcham, T. 1997. Salthill Quarry Geology Trail. *Geologists' Association Guide*, **58**, *30 pp.*

Bray, A. 1927. The Carboniferous sequence between Lothersdale and Cowling (Colne). *Journal of the Manchester Geological Association, Vol.* **1**, *pp. 44-57.*

Hudson, R. G. S. & Mitchell, G. H. (1937): The Carboniferous geology of the Skipton Anticline. *Geological Survey of Great Britain, Summary of Progress for 1935, part* **2***, pp. 1-45.*

Miller, J. & Grayson, R. F. (1972): Origin and structure of the Lower Viséan "reef" limestones near Clitheroe, Lancashire. *Proceedings of the Yorkshire Geological Society, Vol.* **38***, pp. 607-638.*

Parkinson, D. (1936): The Carboniferous succession in the Slaidburn district, Yorkshire. *Quarterly Journal of the Geological Society, London,* **92***, pp. 294-331.*

Riley, N. J., Varker, W. J., Owens, B., Higgins, A. C., Ramsbottom, W. H. C. (1987): Stonehead Beck, Cowling, North Yorkshire, England: A British Proposal for the Mid-Carboniferous Boundary Stratotype. *Courier Forschungsinstitut Senckenberg,* **98***, 159-178.*

FOSSIL PLATES

Paul Kabrna and Jeremy J. Savill

The aim of the plates is to illustrate some of the common fossils you may come across during an excursion. Another consideration when constructing the plates was to represent as many different fossil groups as possible. The absence of bivalves and echinoderms from the plates is due to the fact that some common bivalves appear in Chapter 2, whilst the echinoderms are comprehensively described in Chapter 3.

PLATE 1

Fig. A.   *Brachymetopus maccoyi*
Dorsal view of a trilobite cephalon.
Whitewell, Bellman Limestone Member.

Fig. B.   *Phillibole aprathensis*
Dorsal view of a complete trilobite carapace.
Salterforth, Bowland Shale Formation.

Fig. C.   *Euomphalus pentangulatus*
Dorsal and ventral views of the gastropod.
Clitheroe, Coplow Quarry, Coplow Limestone Member.

Fig. D.   *Antiquatonia hindi*
Pedicle valve of a productid brachiopod.
Clitheroe, Salthill Quarry, Bellman Limestone Member.

Fig. E.   *Dictyoclostus semireticulatus*
Pedicle valve of a productid brachiopod.
Clitheroe, Salthill Quarry, Bellman Limestone Member.

Scale bars 10 mm

PLATE 2

Brachiopods

Fig. A.   *Spirifer*
Pedicle valve and brachial valve.
Whitewell, Bellman Limestone Member.

Fig. B.   *Nebenothyris* sp.
Pedicle valve and brachial valve.
Whitewell, Bellman Limestone Member.

Fig. C.   *Pugnax*
Pedicle valve and brachial valve.
Clitheroe, Salthill Quarry, Bellman Limestone Member.

Fig. D.   *Pleuropugnoides*
Pedicle valve and brachial valve.
Whitewell, Bellman Limestone Member.

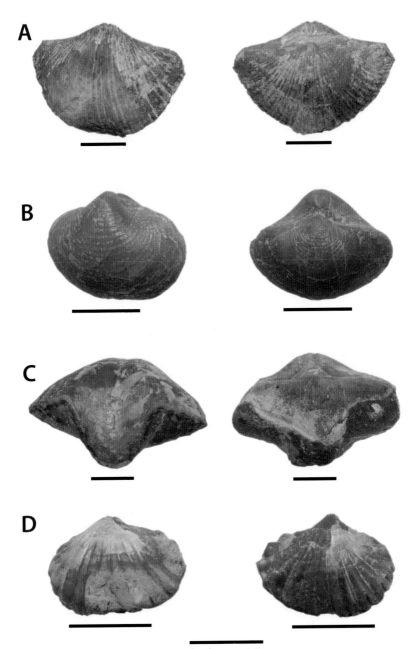

Scale bars 10 mm

PLATE 3

Fig. A.   *Amplexus coralloides*
Solitary rugose coral: longitudinal and polished top view.
Clitheroe, Coplow Quarry, Coplow Limestone Member.

Fig. B.   *Caninia*
Solitary rugose coral: longitudinal and polished top view.
Clitheroe, Salthill Quarry, Bellman Limestone Member.

Fig. C.   *Michelina*
Tabulate coral showing both longitudinal and top view.
Clitheroe, Salthill Quarry, Bellman Limestone Member.

Fig. D.   Goniatite
A well developed suture is shown by the wavy lines.
Slaidburn, Bowland Shale Formation.

Fig. E.   *Fenestella*
Bryozoa showing the characteristic mesh-like structure.
Clitheroe, Coplow Quarry, Coplow Limestone Member.

Scale bars 10 mm